MASTER MIND MASTER LIFE

NORMAN PLOTKIN

For information contact www.normanplotkin.com

Cover design by Jasmine Hromjak
Editing: Laurie Chittenden
Author photo courtesy of Michael Roud, Michael Roud Photography, Los Angeles, CA

ISBN: 978-1-7352354-0-0

Published 2020

To Tian: Goddess, friend, soulmate.
Your support, your leadership, your inspiration
have been the difference between this book
living in my head and the words making it onto paper.
The next one we write together!

CONTENTS

FOREWORD

When I finished reading Norman's manuscript this morning, I turned the lights low in my office and began to do some deep breathing and meditation. As a colleague of Norm's and a former recipient of hypnotherapy, I have learned how to strengthen and deepen suggestions facilitated in past sessions. How powerful is that?!; learning to take control of something that can feel out of control without hours and hours of talk therapy, or using medications that may have harmful side effects! Don't get me wrong, as a psychologist and a coach running a private practice, I believe there is a place for traditional therapies and medication. However, sometimes these strategies are not enough. As knowledge in medical and mental health professions have evolved along-side of technology, we have become more and more aware of the impact stress and trauma can have on our nervous systems and our over-all health in general. As Norman states, "life is a contact sport and not only do none of us get out alive, we pick up a lot of scars and baggage along the way." When we get disconnected from the root cause of our traumas or scars, we become increasingly prone to illness and engaging in bad habits and harmful behaviors. Over the years, I have had many people walk into my offices asking, "Why do I continue to eat so much, or binge drink, or smoke, when I know it is hurting me?" Usually they are engaging in maladaptive behaviors to manage symptoms of something that they are not fully aware of. As humans, we have inborn defense mechanisms that help us block out stresses and traumas that we do not always have the ego strength to deal with in the moment. Defense mechanisms are necessary and helpful. They can also become ingrained and problematic over our life span. The process of hypnotherapy creates conditions that bypass defense mechanisms and allow us not only to expel stress and trauma from our nervous systems, but incorporate new thoughts and behaviors, that greatly improve physical health, mental health, and performance through the power of suggestion.

Norman Plotkin has extensive training and experience in hypnotherapy. He has been able to help people all over the world by use of video conference platforms. As you will see in reading this book, he has gone far beyond sharing the basics of hypnotherapy by integrating personal experience, case studies, and the most up to date research and information available in a very relatable way. He traces the "trance" state in hypnotherapy as common to healers throughout history in every culture. And the exciting current day news is that we can measure the efficacy of hypnotherapy through modern technologies such as magnetic resonance imaging (MRI) and electroencephalography (EEG). Neuroscience has truly legitimized hypnotherapy as an effective treatment modality. Norman cites reports from the national institute of health (NIH) supporting use of hypnosis for pain management, irritable bowel syndrome, tension headaches, and stress reduction. In addition, he cites applications for behavioral change, such as smoking cessation, weight loss, sports performance, test preparation and various other habit control measures.

If you are curious about the mechanisms of hypnotherapy or struggling with a condition, harmful habit, or undesirable behavior that you have been unable to get a grip on, this book is a must read for you. Hypnotherapy is an efficient, noninvasive modality that will free you from pain and suffering and greatly improve the quality of your life!

DAVID HOY, PhD
Author of *Getting Into A Good College*
May Not Be As Hard As You Think
Executive Director David Hoy & Associates

INTRODUCTION

"As you sow in your subconscious mind, so shall you reap in your body and environment."—JOSEPH MURPHY

I've wanted to write about hypnotherapy since I began studying the subject. This book, more than five years in the making, is based on my schooling, as well as independent study of the history, scholarship, research and anecdotes about hypnotherapy. While client names have been changed and private details were kept to a minimum, I include personal stories to bring the experiences home in a way that others can identify with and realize are very real.

My goal is to make hypnotherapy understandable and approachable since the modality is all too often mocked and maligned. There is so much misinformation out there that it is important to me to present the facts that show how hypnotherapy really works and how very effective it can be when used correctly. What follows is a proper introduction to the hypnotherapy modality.

I truly believe everyone can be helped by hypnotherapy. Life is a contact sport. None of us gets out alive and, along the way, we gather scars and baggage. At fifty-five years old I know this to be true.

Growing up in a rural town on a ranch, I come from a story-telling tradition. After college when I went to work for the state legislature as an analyst and later as a lobbyist, I constantly told stories. Storytelling is at the heart of persuasion and engages the listener in the content. Everyone loves a good story, a sentiment that is at the heart of the success of books, movies and shows of all kinds. What I know now is that I was unconsciously employing conversational hypnosis! So it is no wonder I have found my way to this remarkable modality.

There is a difference between a hypnotist and a hypnotherapist. Hypnotists are the folks you see at the state fair or on stage in Las Vegas. All hypnosis is self-hypnosis. You can enter a trance every day, but only a hypnotherapist can facilitate deep, rich therapeutic work during the state, or trance. A big difference! A hypnotherapist has been trained and certified by an accredited institution like The Hypnosis Motivation Institute (HMI) in Los Angeles. There is no substitute for adequate training, and there is no better institution than HMI, in my opinion. The distinction between a hypnotist and a hypnotherapist is an important point.

If you want to learn about the what, where, when, why and how of hypnotherapy, this book will answer those questions. Malcolm Gladwell has a theory that if you engage in an endeavor for 10,000 hours you can gain mastery. I just surpassed my 10,000-hour mark doing hypnotherapy, so perhaps I have achieved mastery. Of course, the same skeptical scientists who look askance at hypnotherapy have written a paper debunking Gladwell's theory of mastery. Nevertheless, I am undeterred. I share with you here details about the amazing modality of hypnotherapy, my personal experiences, my thoughts and my perspective.

This is not a scientific paper, nor is it a scholarly article. This book does not constitute research, is not a book laden with research, and I do not have an impressive list of citations at the end. There are a few references and some citations when I have pointed to the work of others directly. Much of this information is in the public domain, but I wanted to write a book that regular people might feel more comfortable reading.

I hope these pages open minds to the possibilities of what hypnotherapy might hold for them and those they love in relation to health, wellness and general wellbeing.

Read on and see for yourself what hypnotherapy is all about and how you might put it to use in your life. Be curious and look around at other resources. There is endless upside to utilizing hypnotherapy and very little, if any, downside. Be prepared though, as powerful as this modality is, it does require that those wishing to benefit from it be ready for change, want change, and be willing to do some powerful change work. As you will see, the mind and body like the known, and the unknown is scary. We will hold onto behavior that does not serve us just because that behavior is familiar. Change might make you very uncomfortable initially. But if you can push past the discomfort, you can become the master of your mind and your body and put yourself on the path to your best life.

In the words of the immortal Lao Tzu, "The journey of a thousand miles begins with the first step." Let this book serve as the first step in your journey - or add to what you know already. Please read on and discover hypnotherapy. When you're done, if you want to know more or you want to put hypnotherapy to work for you, reach out. You can find my contact information at the back of the book.

CHAPTER ONE

If My Mind Is So Powerful Why Can't I Change/Heal On My Own?

Janice was 72 years old. She called and desperately asked if I could help her with a long list of maladies: Lyme disease, mast cell disease (Systemic Mastocytosis), auto-immune symptoms. She said she couldn't leave the house. Her children couldn't visit. She was allergic to everything. On top of all of that, and as a result of all of that, she was both anxious and depressed. When I asked her how stressed she felt, she put her level at 9.5 out of 10.

I listened and took copious consultation notes. As I did so, I considered all my training and experience. What could I do or say to help this poor woman? The first thing I *had* to say was that I needed a referral from her physician because my scope of practice requires that if there is a medical ideation or psychological origin to a presenting issue, I must have a referral from the treating physician or mental health practitioner. She wasn't happy she had to jump through that hoop, but I said I was ethically bound to follow the rules and that it was for her own safety.

Most physicians scoff at the idea of writing a referral to a hypnotherapist and only relent if their patient is adamant. Often what I see is a note that says hypnotherapy is not contra-indicated for the underlying condition (usually because I have given the physician that option when they balk at a referral). Janice obtained the referral and we set up a session by video conference since she couldn't leave the house.

In Janice's initial session, as with all of my initial sessions, we started with a deep dive into her history from childhood to present. I was looking for traumas, traumatic events and experiences likely to have left a lasting impression and/or cause repressed emotions.

Her childhood was difficult with a working class, alcoholic father and a mother who often experienced depression that stemmed from marrying a man she didn't really love who was verbally and physically abusive. Her parents had three children and raised them the best they could. However, Janice's childhood didn't seem to be at the heart of her health issues.

I asked her when her health troubles began. She said she thought the Lyme disease started after she was at a little league baseball park. I said I wasn't asking her when she thought she was bitten by a tick; I was asking what was going on in her life when the health issues arose. She hemmed and hawed, she obfuscated and resisted. I knew I was getting closer. Then she blurted out, "I had an affair!"

Now we were on to something! I asked her if she was Catholic. She replied she was. I asked her if she had confessed and asked for forgiveness. She said yes, she had confessed and asked for forgiveness. I asked her if she thought God had forgiven her. She said yes, she thought God had forgiven her. So, I asked if God could forgive her, why couldn't she forgive herself?

Over the course of the next few sessions we worked on forgiveness and releasing guilt. Her anxiety lowered. Her depression subsided. And her symptoms began to recede. She told me she felt like she got her life back. We can become prisoners of our own repressed emotions. But Janice never connected the extra-marital affair and the shame, blame and guilt associated with it to her health issues.

Debbie was in her fifties. She had raised her kids and held a great job in the legislature with a good deal of responsibility. Eight years before she came to see me, she had been diagnosed with fibromyalgia. She had excellent healthcare benefits and access to the best doctors. Having worked for a medical association and now the legislative health committee, she knew many top doctors. However, the care she received was limited to pain management. She took opioids to control the pain from the autoimmune symptoms for eight years, but then she had enough of the pills and stopped taking them. She had a hard time getting up in the morning. Debbie had been a very social person all of her life, yet she hadn't been out with friends in a very long time. She saw an acupuncturist with some success, and more than one therapist, but the pain persisted, compounded by a level of depression that this state had become her life. As many do, she tried everything before coming to me as a last resort.

Debbie was a veteran, having served in the Air Force. She was very nice, but she grew up in a tough neighborhood and thus presented herself as a tough individual. Having been referred by a friend who had seen me and had excellent outcomes, she approached hypnotherapy with an open mind.

We looked at the history of her life, going back to her childhood. Then, together, in the first session we worked on some inner-child exercises and in the next session I asked her to create a garden of her life where we raked all of the dead old leaves that represented people and events that hurt her into a big pile and burned them, then we planted new seeds. This represented the end of her old story that was the source of her pain and the creation of a new story, a new story she could nurture without the pain.

As I got to know her, I came to understand that although she had a tough (but friendly) exterior, inside she was a marshmallow - soft and feminine and loving. When we focused on her divorce I came to a realization. Tough physically, but soft emotionally, Debbie had somatized the emotional pain of her divorce into her physically tough body. This pain manifested as auto-immune symptoms. She would not let go of these pain symptoms because her subconscious mind feared she would then experience what it had been hiding from for many years: deep emotional pain around the end of her relationship with the father of her children.

I asked her if she was ready to let go of the pain. She said if it were that easy, she would have done it years ago. I asked again if she was ready. She agreed. I had her tell me what it would feel like to be pain free. I asked her to tell me how it would feel in her body and give the pain free feeling a color. I asked her about all the things she would do when she was free from the pain. In hypnosis, I asked her to envision a life free of pain. I preconditioned her to an ideomotor response by telling her to put all of the pain in one arm so that it would become rigid. After releasing the pain in the arm, I had her again envision a life free of pain; I had her see herself doing all of the things she told me she would do; I had her see the color of being pain free. Then I told her that when she was ready to let go of the pain for good, her arm would begin to lift and rise. It took a while, and a couple of attempts, this was powerful stuff, but her arm began to lift and rise. I had her again feel her body pain free, see herself doing all of the things she said she would do (the whole time leaving her arm up). And when I brought her out of hypnosis, the first thing she saw was her arm in the air, which was a subconscious demonstration that she was done with the pain. The look on her face was priceless.

The next week when I checked in to see if Debbie was ready for a follow up session she said yes. I held my breath as I asked her what she wanted to work on. Her reply? Motivation! She said she had been depressed and sleeping in for so long, she needed help getting her mostly pain free ass up and out into the world!

I was drawn to hypnotherapy after my own health issues. In 2011, I was diagnosed with papillary carcinoma, thyroid cancer, and had a radical thyroidectomy and lymph node resection - a surgeon removed my thyroid and five lymph nodes. The surgery was followed over the next year by two rounds of radiation.

Before I was a hypnotherapist or a lobbyist, I was a legislative analyst and I was very good at analyzing complex issues and getting to the root of the matter. I applied the same type of rigorous review to my health situation. I wanted to understand how we produce disease and how we can manage it and even overcome it.

I compiled what I found during that rigorous review into my first book, *Take Charge of Your Cancer, The Seven Proven Steps to Healing and Recovery.* In doing the research for that book I discovered how powerful the subconscious mind is and how it not only controls every aspect of our life, but also that it becomes programmed just like a computer that gets set, often early in our lives, and it can be extremely difficult to change.

Too often, we try to suppress unwanted feelings and behavior by masking them with chemical therapy. Many then become a slave to the drugs. In my opinion, chemical therapy only disguises the underlying conditions and puts off dealing with the actual problem(s) thus never allowing one to get better. I wanted to go in another direction. I wanted to help others with what I learned. This was the way I made sense of my own experience with cancer. I found meaning in the experience by using it to put myself into the service of others.

It was important to me that this service be organic, non-invasive and non-chemical. Hypnotherapy met all of those conditions. It has been around since the beginning of the human experience. Despite mockery by Hollywood and those afraid of hypnotherapy, those who don't understand it, or those who mistakenly believe that for something to be efficacious it has to be exceedingly complex, hypnotherapy proves beneficial on a daily basis to multitudes of people from all walks of life and across all cultures.

Are we really the objects of programming like a computer? From the time we are born until about the age of 10 we are, for all intents and purposes, in a state of hypnosis. We are highly suggestible and we mirror and match people who are in our sphere of influence. We make decisions as a child to adapt to a subjectively accepting family. As children, we're highly dependent on our caretakers for safety, support, comfort, and guidance. We learn early on that it is essential to securely bond with those in our immediate sphere of influence, most of whom are our family members.

We undertake these adaptive tactics that are dependency-rooted and that are understandable in the context of our childhood. But as an adult, we must reevaluate what we earlier deemed crucial to getting along with our family members, fitting in with our peers and even survival. The problem is you may not even realize the ways you felt obliged to fit in. The programming is often subtle.

The not so subtle evidence of the programming can be recognized in the words of our parents and others. Words and phrases like: *money doesn't grow on trees, you never live up to your potential, why can't you be more like your brother/sister?* And worse. To be sure, there are positive phrases and programming running through our minds as well, but it is those pesky negative narratives that hold us back, trip us up, or worse, make us sick. Now I explore childhood with all clients and do a session on their inner child to transcend the limiting dialogue that universally lingers.

I was watching a show on Gaia.com recently called *Rewired* with Dr. Joe Dispenza. Dr. Joe is an amazing individual with an amazing story of recovery and healing from a tragic life-threatening accident. He also attended Hypnosis Motivation Institute where I received my training. Dr. Joe has gone on to do some remarkable work with brain studies, diving deep into the how and why of behavior and programming. *Rewired* shares a lot of what he discovered.

In the episode I was watching, Dr. Joe asked why we talk about a better life but seem unable to change at a deeper level, in other words, why do so many of us wait for crisis, trauma, disease, diagnosis, betrayal or loss? This resonated with me as it took a diagnosis of cancer, radical organ removal and radiation to wake me up. He went on to ask if it wouldn't be better to change in a state of joy and inspiration than in a state of pain and suffering. Which state would you choose to undertake to change the pain of yesterday into the joy of tomorrow?

During the program there was a deep discussion about how the brain and body react to change. At the core of the conversation was the indisputable fact that thoughts create your life. We have approximately 60,000 to 70,000 thoughts per day and 90 percent of them are exactly the same as they were the day before. What this means is you are not going to change because the same thoughts lead to the same choices, which lead to the same behavior, which lead to the same experiences, which lead to the same emotions, which give rise to the same thoughts in a sometimes pathetically predictable feedback loop.

Your biology stays the same: your neurochemistry, your neurocircuitry, your hormones and your gene expression. When our biology stays the same so does our personality, because our personality is how we think, act and feel. By the time we are 35 years old our brain becomes hard-wired and this is our identity. We are a set of programs, memorized behaviors, unconscious emotional reactions, automatic habits, hard-wired beliefs, attitudes and perceptions.

The first step toward change is to know yourself. Know you are human with very human attributes. And, like everyone else, you will get caught in the feedback loop described above if you don't make a conscious decision to define a vision for your life by overcoming the tendency to live on autopilot, which is a collection of the same memorized behaviors you've carried out for most of your life. Part of this self-knowledge includes an understanding of the conscious and subconscious minds and the parts they play in our thoughts, actions and behaviors. We will go into greater detail in Chapter Three, but for now the following illustration might be helpful.

Perhaps you have seen the graphic of the iceberg and the ocean. Ninety to ninety-five percent of the iceberg is below the surface of the water. This is like the subconscious mind. The conscious mind, the part of the mind characterized by logic, reason, analysis, decision making and will power, is the five to ten percent tip of the iceberg. The other 90-95 percent, the subconscious, controls our involuntary bodily functions, our pulse, temperature, heartbeat and hormones, our autonomic nervous system. We don't have to think about breathing or maintaining a temperature of 98.6.

The same part of the mind helps us internalize behaviors so that we do not have to think about walking, or riding a bike, or driving a car. These become the programs that run below the surface of our thinking and free us up to earn a living, keep shelter over our heads and put food on the table. The logical conscious mind conducts an analysis of all environmental stimuli and checks it against the subconscious programming. If it is consistent with the programming, it is accepted. If it is not consistent, the conscious mind rejects it through a rationalization.

Resistance, then, emerges when a thought or desired action or behavior does not align with our subconscious programming. Examples of resistance are things like not following through, not practicing, and self-sabotage. The mind and body want to avoid rocking the boat. Biologically, this is referred to as homeostasis, but the subconscious wants to maintain a behavioral homeostasis, as well.

The known world is good, safe and on the pleasure side of the pleasure/pain continuum. The unknown, on the other hand, is likely to trigger that survival-based mechanism of the autonomic nervous system, the fight or flight response. So, no matter how bad we think we want to change, our mind and body are going to conspire to resist and revert us back to those hard-wired, memorized behaviors, unconscious emotional reactions, automatic habits, hard-wired beliefs, attitudes and perceptions. This is why hypnotherapy is so powerful. It can bypass the resistance and help achieve rapid change and transformation. Despite the effectiveness of hypnosis and its long history of application to healing, many people tend to fear it as a loss of control, or mock it as hocus pocus.

Hypnotic states have been used for healing for as long as humankind has existed, but because most people's exposure to hypnosis is likely to be in an entertainment venue, perhaps a stage show where people cluck like a chicken or eat an onion and think it's an apple, there is a lack of trust and understanding. Moreover, hypnosis has been portrayed in Hollywood and on television and in the media as something mysterious and magical, supposedly out of the hypnotic subject's control and, consequently, it has been viewed with distrust and skepticism by many in the general public and especially by many health professionals.

For example, the movie *Get Out* portrayed a character who was asked if he wanted to be hypnotized by his girlfriend's mother who was a psychiatrist in order to stop smoking. His response was, "Nah, I'm all right." At that point, he wouldn't be open to being hypnotized since it is very difficult to make someone do something against their will. Instead, the movie plot has the psychiatrist induce a hypnotic trance by tinkling her spoon against her teacup and magically transporting the unsuspecting character to a "sunken place." A flagrant example of artistic license at the expense of legitimate hypnotherapy.

When the conditions are right, when the hypnotherapist is properly trained and establishes a rapport with the client; when the client is serious about doing the work and sincerely desires the sought-after change, or healing, there is endless possibility. The power of the subconscious mind is capable of amazing feats.

The biggest hurdle is getting past people's tendency to make things more complicated than they need to be. Complex machines, elaborate chemical therapies and complicated theories are not always necessary to accomplish great things. Sometimes all that is needed is a little belief and faith, a little trust and the rapport between a skilled hypnotherapist and a client ready to make real change in their life.

In the following pages we are going to explore where hypnosis came from, its origins and earliest applications as well as its presence across different cosmologies. We will look at exactly what the modality is, and what is going on in the body when someone is in trance. We will examine what science has to say about hypnosis and what the evidence-based health community thinks about the process through their studies, rather than how hypnosis is portrayed by Hollywood.

The discussion will continue with an examination of the many uses of hypnotherapy from the general to the specific, and then move into how you might use hypnotherapy in your life. I will give examples from scholarly articles, research, books and my own clinical practice. My hope is that reading this book on hypnotherapy will leave you in the same state of awe I am in as I practice this magnificent modality to help others make positive changes in their lives. The near daily ah-ha moments that my clients have makes this the most satisfying thing I have ever done.

So, let's dive in, shall we?

CHAPTER TWO

Where Did Hypnosis Come From?

As I discuss the history of hypnotherapy I am going to stay away from references to it in movies, television and on stage, such as the 1949 movie with Orson Welles called *Black Magic* or the vaudeville acts during the 1920's. Although one stage performer from the vaudeville days, Dave Elman, went on to become an influential hypnotherapist later in life and wrote a classic manual called *Hypnotherapy*.

Eye fascination, which was an early induction technique, and is still used today in certain circumstances, has been characterized by the swinging pocket watch and accompanied by the words, "You are getting sleepier and sleepier." The technique has become an instantly recognized representation of hypnosis at various places like county fairs or in Las Vegas and it is often still most people's first impression. Unfortunately, these examples all detract from the power of hypnotherapy for change and healing that many ancient civilizations and scientists have utilized for centuries.

In fact, throughout the history of humankind, every culture and every tribe has had their own version of healer or healers. Nearly all ancient cultures and indigenous tribes across the globe had their own collection of ceremonial techniques and ritual practices. And there were common elements across these cultures, similar techniques discovered by medicine people from every corner of the planet. Despite having no contact with each other, amazingly similar practices evolved--and in some places are still practiced today.

Among these near universal practices was the inducement of trance, or a trance state. In the shamanic tradition, it is referred to as non-ordinary reality. Trance work has transcended various cosmologies around the world and is experiential and very personal. These ancient, almost universal practices all employed the very components necessary for hypnotic trance: sensory overload, expectation, and suggestion in their rituals to heal and predict.

Since ancient times, healers have been aware of the effect of words and ideas on a person's health and well-being. Words and ideas can and do have a direct and dynamic impact on physiology. This is sometimes referred to as ideodynamic to designate the relationship between words and a corresponding dynamic physiological response. As I did with the client I told you about earlier in the book, Debbie, in which I instructed her to put her pain into one arm and then we raised and lowered her arm.

I learned from courses at Hypnosis Motivation Institute that as far back as 1,500 B.C.E., in the Western tradition, there is documentation from Egypt in the *Papyrus Ebers* that describes healing evoked by the practice of magical incantation and ritual that facilitated the experience of altered states, belief, and expectancy. The Temple of Imhotep, in the ancient city of Saqqara, was an important healing center. Among the Egyptian practices was a tradition called temple sleep. People who didn't feel well journeyed to the temple in search of healing from the gods. After long rituals of ingesting herbs and rhythmically incanting prayers for hours, the person was led to a special darkened chamber to sleep and await a dream that revealed a cure. The practice spread to Greece where they built special sleep temples dedicated to Aesclapius, the god of healing. As in Egypt, Greek sufferers journeyed to the temple to undergo the proper rituals and dream of a cure in a sleep chamber.

It is easy to understand now that the divine answers and feelings of reassurance experienced by ancient peoples were the product of sensory overload, expectation and direct suggestion, but that does not diminish the physical and emotional healing that took place because of these processes, all of which formed the foundation of trance.

The use of trance states was also used in the ancient practice of oracles. Oracles were people employed by temples to predict the future. Like sleep temples in Egypt and Greece, the person's expectation and overload were essential ingredients in creating hypnotic states. These were accomplished through preparatory practices including the drinking of herbal mixtures and the imagery of chambers filled with candles and brightly painted images, much like the extravagant cathedrals and temples of religious traditions throughout the ages. The result of this elaborate ritual was a heightened suggestibility in the person's mind, creating a foundation for an exceptional emotional experience.

Other cultures have carried out these types of ideodynamic healing rituals through *shamans, curanderos, pajes, strega, maes de santo* and countless other names. All carry on a remarkable tradition as keepers of ancient techniques used to achieve and maintain well-being and healing for themselves as well as members of their community. What is most amazing is that these techniques are strikingly similar the world over among cultures separated by time, space and geography, and a near universal common thread of ideodynamic healing through trance.

In the West, these practices continued largely unchanged until the Middle Ages when early philosopher-physicians like Magnus, Paracelsus and Fludd carried on healing utilizing incantations, faith and essentially magical or archetypal belief systems.

The term mesmerized is fairly well understood today to mean that someone is fixated on someone or something in a trance-like state. The term derives from Franz Anton Mesmer who produced his first theories of mesmerism in the middle eighteenth century. In 1774, during a magnetic treatment with a female patient, Mesmer felt he perceived a fluid flowing through the woman's body that was affected by his own will. He eventually named this fluid and its manipulation "Animal Magnetism" and developed an elaborate theory regarding its effect on health. The theory described a natural energy transference that occurs between all animate and inanimate objects. As an extension of this theory he believed he could magnetize people into his control and grew quite a following. Some of his followers bought into the concept of magnetism, while others believed that the state of control characterized by mesmerism was due to other factors, including Mesmer's personality.

By the mid-1780s, Mesmer's dramatic practices had drawn the amazement and scrutiny of the citizens of Paris, including that of King Louis XVI himself, who commissioned a panel of renowned scientists to examine Animal Magnetism to ascertain whether it was fact or fiction. Louis XVI's panel included medical doctors from the Royal Faculty of Medicine in Paris as well as respected scientists from other fields. These included the chemist Antoine Lavoisier – discoverer of oxygen and hydrogen; Dr. Joseph Guillotine – co-founder of the Academy of Medicine in Paris and the inventor of the guillotine; astronomer Jean Bailly, a senior member of the French Academy of Sciences who studied the moons of Jupiter; and American scientist and Ambassador to France, Benjamin Franklin.

After months of investigation and observation, the commission determined that Mesmer had not discovered a real physical fluid, that the human body did not contain previously undiscovered channels, and that any effects of his treatments were due solely to the "imagination" of the subjects.

Today the word "mesmerism" generally functions as a synonym of "hypnosis." In 1843, however, the Scottish doctor James Braid departed from Mesmer and proposed the term "hypnosis," which is a Greek term for sleep, for the technique he derived from what had previously been referred to as animal magnetism. While observing hypnotized patients, Braid observed many physiological changes. Among these changes was rapid eye movement, shallow breathing, and passivity as the subject entered the deeper state, which happened to closely resemble sleep.

Braid noticed that during this state his patients were easily influenced by verbal suggestions, even to the point of controlling involuntary functions. These observations compared to tests with patients not under hypnosis led Braid to conclude his hypnotized patients were more receptive to his suggestions than those not in a hypnotic state.

After Mesmer and Braid, there followed a period of experiment and discovery. Chevreul, a French chemist, published an experimental critique of the ancient beliefs and uses of devices of divination. Chevreul was followed by Bernheim, a French professor of medicine who recognized that hypnosis, or what he referred to as suggestive therapeutics, by its essential nature, was an ideodynamic process and wrote:

> *The mechanism of suggestion in general may then*
> *be summed up in the following formula: increase of*
> *the reflex ideomotor, ideosensitive, and ideosensorial*

excitability ... is increased in the brain, so that any idea received is immediately transformed into an act, without the controlling portion of the brain, the higher centers, being able to prevent the transformation. (Bernheim, 1886/1957, pp. 137-139)

Bernheim's vernacular is a bit dated, but he quite insightfully describes information transduction as a basic process of therapeutic hypnotherapy. Indeed, all modern mind/body healing modalities attempt to facilitate this process of converting words, images, sensations, beliefs, ideas and expectations into the physiological healing of the body.

Scientists around Europe were experimenting with the process in ever greater numbers. For the last half of the 19th Century, the greatest amount of research and academic debate came out of France, spurred on by a spirited rivalry between two dramatically conflicting schools of thought. The Nancy School, led by Ambroise Liebeault and Hippolyte Bernheim, and the Salpetriere School, led by Jean- Martin Charcot.

The study and use of hypnosis and hypnotherapy continued into the modern era. The lineage included Braid, Breuer, Freud, Jung and Erickson. In early experiments by Freud and Jung, their forceful, authoritarian approach to hypnotic induction led some patients to fabricate memories. There was a departure at this point in time and while hypnotherapy was carried on and its exploration and therapeutic application continued,

Breuer, Freud and Jung forged a new path in the direction of psychoanalysis.

On the therapeutic hypnosis front, Milton Erickson pioneered what is commonly referred to as the utilization approach, which is a permissive, exploratory and ideodynamic approach to therapeutic hypnosis. This utilization approach eliminated the types of emotional pressures on patients that led them to make up responses. Erickson became one of the most well-known hypnotherapists of the 20th Century. Stricken with polio as a youth, he used a self-taught form of self-hypnosis to help overcome the pain and stiffness associated with the disease. Erickson's unique therapeutic style and techniques have become a popular genre in hypnotherapy today, though aspects are viewed by some as controversial, such as the use of covert hypnotic inductions. Erickson taught many physicians over the years. One story goes that because he was masterful at the handshake induction, most were afraid to greet him with a handshake.

Modern science has given us a variety of tools for observing, measuring and quantifying physiological responses. These processes for validation gave rise to what is referred to as evidence-based medicine. Historically, practitioners of hypnotherapy have presented evidence of biological healing in the form of clinical case studies and histories. Skeptical scientists who typically require well-documented laboratory experimentation have largely remained unconvinced about the effectiveness of hypnotherapy absent scientific criteria for validity.

In the skeptic's view, so-called therapeutic hypnosis is a form of placebo, or in other words, a nuisance variable. We will explore the placebo effect later, as well as what science has to say about hypnosis, but expectation and the placebo effect are real, and not necessarily a derogatory condition. Nevertheless, the skeptics view hypnotherapy as an unreliable, not necessarily repeatable, spontaneous healing phenomenon due to as yet unknown factors that lead the therapist to believe that his or her suggestions have somehow led to healing.

The controversy has carried on without a satisfactory solution because until recently we have not been able to offer compelling scientific proof of physiological response characteristics sufficient to quell the skeptics. If you ask someone who has experienced healing from therapeutic hypnosis, they will unequivocally tell you about their experience. Insofar as this is subjective and until recently has been unsubstantiated, it is seen as little more than anecdote. But breakthroughs in areas such as psychosomatic medicine, the neurobiology of emotion, learning and memory, molecular genetics and the endocrinology of stress along with enhanced imaging capabilities like functional magnetic resonance imaging have given us tools for objective measurement and documentation.

We will explore in greater depth what science has to say about therapeutic hypnosis later in chapter four.

Today, there are a multitude of applications for hypnotherapy ranging from stress and anxiety reduction to achieving health, wellness and wellbeing, discussed more in chapter five.

The world is increasingly designed to keep us in a state of hypnosis. There is an argument that in our 24/7 wired modern environment most people are walking around in a state of hypnosis and are highly suggestable. Being in a trance is good for the economy! If we were not suggestable to thoughts that we were lacking or unhappy, why would we need more? How do you sell anti-aging products? You make people worry about getting old. How do you get people to buy insurance? You get them to be fearful of everything! How do you get people to undergo plastic surgery? By emphasizing their physical flaws. How do you get them to see the latest blockbuster movie? By making them fearful of missing out (there's even an acronym for that one: FOMO). How do you get people to buy the latest technological gadget? By making them feel like others are leaving them behind.

Oftentimes I have to dehypnotize people who have literally been programmed by the media and society. One example of going into hypnosis in your regular experience is when you drive home from work and zone out. You do not remember the drive, and all of a sudden you are in your driveway. You were in hypnosis. Radio advertisers know this, which is why commute time advertising is so expensive.

CHAPTER THREE

What the Hell Is Hypnosis?

It has been my experience with clients over the years that most people do not really care what is going on within the world of hypnotherapy as long as it works for them. But there are some who want to better understand the forces at work and why they work and why they are even necessary in the first place. No matter where you are in that framework, a book about hypnotherapy rightly ought to have a discussion about what is going on in the body during hypnosis so what follows is a discussion of the physiology associated with hypnosis from a non-scientific point of view.

How do our physical brains produce our subjective experience? This question is really at the heart of the puzzle that has challenged philosophers and scientists from time immemorial.

The brain is about three pounds of matter. If you take a closer look, you will find distinctive layers, and in looking closer still we find a seemingly infinite tangle of specialized cells. We can objectively observe the three pounds of matter, but when we take stock in the input from our senses, the feel of the warmth of the sun, music from the radio, the smell of coffee, we unlock a subjective world that defines our outer experience. How does three pounds of matter produce objective phenomena like electrochemical impulses moving across synapses, and at the same time create the subjective experiences of sight, sound, smell, etc.? What we are talking about is the age old question of the physical and the psychological, the connection between our inner world and our outer lives.

I was taught that three things must be present for the hypnosis modality to be effective. First there must be authority, the person executing the hypnotic induction must know what they are doing, understand the process, and be trusted by the client as someone who can perform a hypnotic induction. Next, there must be a doctrine, or a paradigm. In other words, there must be a process or theory underlying the practice, a rulebook, an outline of what it is, like a manual. Finally, the person being hypnotized must feel something. Given these criteria for hypnosis to take place, we can look differently at other situations that present a potential hypnotic trance created by expectation and overload, which are nothing more than the client's preconceived notion of what to expect, generally facilitated by what is known as a pre-induction speech (expectation) and the sense engaging details that create the trance by overloading the client's conscious mind and cause them to want to escape into trance (overload).

For example, let's look at a couple common circumstances that have all three requirements for hypnosis, but we don't usually associate them with a hypnotic trance. A lab coat and stethoscope (authority), medical books and medical school (a doctrine), and do you feel something when you go to the doctor? Tests, procedures, shots can all lead to a range of emotions.

Or how about this one? A special collar, robes or hat (authority), a Bible or Torah or Koran (doctrine or paradigm), do you feel something in church or temple?

In a 2006 article in the *American Journal of Psychiatry* titled, *The Process of Hypnotism and the Nature of the Hypnotic State*, authors Lawrence Kubie and Sydney Margolin offer the following explanation of what hypnosis is:

1. The process of inducing hypnosis and the fully developed hypnotic state are a continuum which can be studied satisfactorily only in the novice, and which under such circumstances consists of three stages which shade from one into the next.

2. In the initiation of the process there is a progressive elimination of all channels of sensory-motor communication between the subject and the outside world, with the exception of the channels of communication between the subject and the hypnotist. As a consequence, during this phase the hypnotist becomes temporarily the sole representative of and contact with the outside world.

3. In this essential characteristic, the induction phase parallels the sensory-motor relationships of the infant to the outside world during the earliest phase of infancy, during

which the parents play in the psychology of the infant a role almost identical to that of the hypnotist in the mental life of the subject.

4. The onset of the hypnotic state consists of a partial sleep in which active sensorimotor channels are restricted to those between the subject and the hypnotist.

5. This reduction of sensory-motor channels obliterates the Ego boundaries of the subject and constricts them, which makes inevitable a psychological fusion between hypnotist and subject.

6. This constitutes the second phase in the process, one in which a fusion of subject and hypnotist is achieved, with the result that to the subject the words of the hypnotist become indistinguishable from his own thoughts. It is this in turn which makes possible all of the phenomena of apparent passive suggestibility.

7. At the same time, this same restriction of sensory-motor relationships induces and makes possible states of hypnagogic reverie in which vivid sensory memories and images are released. These images and memories include olfactory, gustatory, tactile, and kinesthetic modalities of sensation which are not ordinarily easily recalled or vividly imagined.

8. The sensory vividness of these reveries in turn opens the way to buried memories, and particularly to the buried affects which are related to such sensory memories.

9. Physiologically, the hypnotic process is shown to be an extension of the processes of normal attention, the result of the creation in the central nervous system of a concentrated focus of excitation with the surrounding areas of inhibition (in the descriptive Pavlovian sense).

10. In turn, this is dependent physiologically upon:

    (a) Relative immobilization through the immobilization of the head or eye.

    (b) The influence of monotony.

11. Initiation of monotony depends upon sensory adaptation, which in turn is in part dependent upon rhythm.

12. Psychologically, the creation of the hypnotic state, with its focus of excitation within limited areas, depends upon a diminution of alertness through allaying anxiety and other defenses, a process that is a necessary prerequisite to the suppression of sensory warning signals.

13. The shift to the fully developed final phase of the hypnotic state involves:

    (a) A partial re-expansion of ego boundaries.

    (b) An incorporation of a fragmentary image of the hypnotist within the expanded boundaries of the subject's Ego.

14. In this final phase the compliance of the subject to the hypnotist's commands is again more apparent than real, in that the incorporated image of the hypnotist which echoes the hypnotist's voice has for the time being become a part of the subject's temporary Ego.

15. It is obvious that the final phase in the hypnotic process, which occurs with the full development of the hypnotic state, parallels precisely that phase in the development of the infant's Ego in which its boundaries gradually expand, with the retention of parental images as unconscious incorporated components of the developing Ego of the infant. The incorporated image of the hypnotist plays the same role in the hypnotic subject as does the

incorporated and unconscious image of the parental figure in the child or adult. Hypnosis thus is seen to be an experimental reproduction of a natural developmental process.

16. The use of hypnosis in some form may conceivably be necessary, therefore, for the complete therapeutic displacement of disturbing superego figures which are retained out of childhood.

17. In the hypnotic process mechanisms are at work identical with those seen in the dream (such as transference, displacement, condensation, etc.). Much has been made of these in the literature; but they are not the essence either of the process or of the state itself.

Generally speaking, hypnosis is a relaxed, yet focused attention very much like deep meditation. We will get into a deeper discussion of the hypnotic state below, but from a high-level perspective, understand that hypnosis evolved in primitive humans as part of the stress response within the autonomic nervous system and its fight or flight mechanism. The sympathetic and parasympathetic systems are designed to react to a threat with certain physiological responses and then reset the body once the threat has subsided.

All of these processes are going on continuously without our conscious mind being aware. Of course, we can be cognizant of a threat, we can feel our heart beat faster and other changes, but rarely do we say to ourselves, "I think I just entered the fight or flight response." These changes going on are subconsciously controlled from within the various parts of the brain.

The brain is the body's central control organ as we all know, but it is only one third of the mind, body, spirit approach. The brain is also extraordinarily complex, and we are coming to understand it in new and important ways. As we come into new understanding, the question often comes up as to whether we can change our body by thought alone. Can our mind be greater than our body and overcome challenges and conditions that arise sometimes of our own making, or that were established in childhood? Does the thought control the mind, or does the mind control the thought? Are the brain and the mind the same? The last couple questions are fun, and probably the subject of another book, so for now, let's have a look at what is going on in hypnosis.

Hypnotherapy is operating on the two aspects of the mind known as the conscious and the subconscious. Actually, it involves bypassing the conscious and speaking to the subconscious. We will dive into these components shortly, but first let's look at the anatomy of the brain and in which part certain activities take place.

The brain has many parts that are responsible for different functions. In the 1960s, American physician and neuroscientist, Paul MacLean, formulated the Triune Brain Model, or three brain theory. Under the Triune Model, the three types of brains are associated with their development in human evolution. The oldest and most closely shared by reptiles, hence referred to as the reptilian brain, is the cerebellum, where all of our automatic responses take place like temperature, heart rate, breathing, etc. The next in the line of evolutionary development is the paleomammalian or emotional brain, otherwise known as the limbic brain; this is where feelings and emotions and their corresponding neurochemistry reside and originate. And finally, the latest arrival on the evolutionary front, the neocortex, which houses several lobes including the frontal, parietal, occipital and temporal. The neocortex is the seat of rational thinking and is responsible for executive function, free will, abstraction, invention and intention.

The inner structures of the brain, as noted above, tend to be older and more primitive. They are responsible for controlling drives, impulses, fears, instincts, emotions, reflexes, subconscious processes, and automatic behaviors. The automatic part of the brain always wants to find balance or equilibrium and will attempt to reset itself toward what is known as homeostasis. This reset is akin to regulating our physiology by bringing the temperature back to 98.6 after a fever or returning to a normal resting heart rate after an environmental stimulus. Similarly, the subconscious wants to keep us in known behavior. This is how we can always remember how to ride a bike or drive a car - we undertake these learned and known behaviors without thinking. While this process is good for riding a bike, driving a car, or playing an instrument, to name a few positive attributes, it is not good for behavior that is learned and known, but not so good for us, like smoking cigarettes, as just one example. This is why it is so hard to quit, or to change other unwanted, learned and known behaviors - the body has given these behaviors over to the autopilot.

So the brain, the autonomic nervous system, and the fight or flight mechanism are critical to understanding hypnosis, but what exactly is hypnosis? Surprisingly, this question is fairly complex. Despite knowing that something is created, a trance, that there are three levels of hypnosis: hypnoidal, catalepsy and somnambulism, a simple definition has been elusive. This could change as our modern electronic monitoring devices allow us to better understand physiological changes of trance, but to date there have been a number of subjective approaches taken. A few of the various attempts by organizations and authors to characterize hypnosis as a healthcare modality through published definitions are discussed below. The common denominator is that there is a hypnotist and a client. Also, it is generally accepted that suggestions are the key ingredient.

As another example of how it has been difficult to agree on a universal definition/description in my opinion missing from these definitions are two critical components that are essential elements in the power of the hypnotic modality: 1) client consent – to be effective, the client has to want to be hypnotized and 2) the intervention must be intended to be helpful.

Some common definitions:

> *Hypnosis can be seen as 'a waking state of awareness, (or consciousness), in which a person's attention is detached from his or her immediate environment and is absorbed by inner experiences such as feelings, cognition and imagery'. Hypnotic induction involves focusing of attention and imaginative involvement to the point where what is being imagined feels real. By the use and acceptance of suggestions, the clinician and patient construct a hypnotic reality. (Williamson, Ann.*

What is Hypnosis and How Might It Work? Palliative Care: Research and Treatment, 2019.)

A situation or set of procedures in which a person designated as the hypnotist suggests that another person designated as the patient experience various changes in sensation, perception, cognition, or control over motor behavior. (Kihlstrom JF. Hypnosis. Annu Rev Psychol. 1985; 36: 385-41)

A hypnotic procedure is a protocol used to establish a hypnotic situation and evaluate responses to it. In such situations, one person (the subject) is guided by another (the hypnotist) to respond to suggestions for alterations in perception, thought, and action. If the constellation of responses to standardized suggestions satisfies a criterion, we infer that the procedure induced a hypnotic state. Hypnotic responses are those responses and experiences characteristic of the hypnotic state. (Killeen PR, Nash MR. The four causes of hypnosis. Int J Clin Exp Hypn. 2003; 51: 195-231.)

Hypnosis (or trance) is an animated, altered, integrated state of focused consciousness (i.e.: controlled imagination). It is an attentive, receptive state of concentration that can be activated readily and measured. It requires some degree of dissociation to enter and become involved in imagined activity, enough concentration for an individual to maintain a certain level of absorption, and some degree of suggestibility to take in new premises. (Spiegel H, Greenleaf M. Commentary: defining hypnosis. Am J Clin Hypn. 2005; 48: 111-116.)

Hypnosis is a state of inner absorption, concentration, and focused attention. It is like using a magnifying glass to focus the rays of the sun and make them more powerful. Similarly, when our minds are concentrated and focused, we are able to use them more powerfully. Because hypnosis allows people to use more of their potential, learning self-hypnosis is the ultimate act of self-control. (Http://www.apa.org/topics/hypnosis/media.aspx.)

Hypnosis is an agreement between a person designated as the hypnotist and a person designated as the client or patient to participate in a psychotherapeutic technique based on the hypnotist providing suggestions for changes in sensation, perception, cognition, affect, mood, or behavior. (Montgomery GH, Hallquist MN, Schnur JB, David D, Silverstein JH, Bovbjerg DH. Mediators of a brief hypnosis intervention to control side effects in breast surgery patients: response expectancies and emotional distress. J Consult Clin Psychol 2010; 78: 80-88.)

As a practical matter, the client will experience a deeply relaxed physical state while at the same time experiencing a heightened state of focus. The heightened state of focus may be intermittently interrupted by a feeling of drifting between the conscious and subconscious aspects of the mind. In the deepest state of hypnosis, somnambulism, the client may experience amnesia, although the subconscious takes in the full experience. There are three levels of hypnosis: hypnoidal, cataleptic and somnambulism. Under new areas of research and thought, dreams are seen to be the fourth and deepest state of trance. This is what hypnosis seeks to replicate.

Hypnosis is quite common, as noted previously, and people experience trance states daily. Examples include getting lost in an exciting movie or a good book, driving home on a familiar stretch of road and not consciously recalling the drive. Similarly, the trance state can also occur when in meditation or prayer, or when undertaking monotonous chores like washing dishes or when in a deeply creative activity like painting. These would be examples of hypnoidal, or the lightest form of hypnosis.

One theory suggests that hypnosis is not a state of consciousness at all; rather, it is an artificial means of accessing the rapid eye movement (REM) state. Under this theory then hypnosis is a process separate from the trance state that it induces, and its effects are no longer mysterious because it is a vehicle to access REM and the dream world. Hypnosis has long been associated with sleep because it is sleep-like, in fact the very word, as we know, is derived from Greek for sleep, but understanding it as a vehicle to access REM gives a previously missing context for this enigmatic process.

When you're dreaming, your ability to move is inhibited for obvious reasons. Physically acting out your dreams could be highly dangerous. This phenomenon of inhibited major muscle movement is known as catalepsy, and it also occurs during hypnosis. This is the most obvious of the parallels between dream sleep and hypnosis. Among others are narrowed attention, activation of inner focus, and the imagination and side-to-side movement of the eyeballs (sometimes, but not always, observed during hypnotic trance).

This trance state is the difference between our conscious awareness of what is around us and an inner awareness. When a person is in these states, their focus is primarily internal, but that doesn't mean we lose our outer awareness. You might consider hypnotherapy a meditative state for a therapeutic purpose, a state that you can learn to access consciously and purposefully.

The hypnotherapist gives suggestions using words, metaphors, or imagery directed at helping the client reach the prearranged, desired outcome.

Hypnotherapy, far from the stage and showmanship hypnosis that occupies so many people's perception, has grown as an integrative modality within the complementary or integrative care offerings of many hospitals. There is a growing body of research, much of it coming out of Stanford University, documenting the physiological explanations of what is at work within the brain in hypnosis, as well as the efficacy of its application as a complementary measure.

The therapy portion of hypnotherapy is related to the actual suggestions offered to the client while in the hypnotic state. The relative skill of the hypnotherapist lies in the ability to place the patient in a trance, the deeper the better, although good results can be achieved in a lighter state, and to then offer relevant suggestions related to the client's issue or concern. The session's relative success is a combination of the relevance of the suggestions, the depth of the trance, and the strength of the therapeutic alliance between the therapist and the client, informally referred to as rapport.

Rapport is extremely critical to the success of hypnotherapy. If a client resists the hypnotherapist, the hypnotherapy will not work, or the person is likely to not even reach the hypnotic state. For hypnotherapy to work, it must be based on a partnership between the therapist and the client. The client must believe in the hypnotherapist's skills and knowledge and trust that person to guide them through the process of uncovering their underlying issue(s) and preparing the right suggestion, metaphor, and or imagery to help the client resolve the issue (s). When rapport is established and trust is held, the work of hypnotherapy can be amazing.

The many and frequent ah-ha moments I have witnessed clients experience when I helped them connect dots that in hindsight seem so obvious, but previously escaped or eluded them for a long time thus creating shame, blame, guilt or worse are truly rewarding. More often than not, the underlying issue is rarely what clients initially come to see me for.

Dana came to see me about her concerns regarding her sugar intake, but after several sessions we discovered it was really about grieving for her deceased mother who had baked for her as a child. The sugar was the way she held onto the memories of her mom. Similarly, Betty came in for weight loss, but together we discovered she was really just trying to please a long-lost parent and food was the avenue. There are also the numerous trauma victims who used food emotionally to keep a layer of protection from the outside world in the form of extra weight. Because the clients trusted me and we were able to establish rapport, as a team, were able to get to the seemingly unconnected issues that were at the foundation of the symptoms.

Let's talk about programming again for a moment. My grandma used to say, "If you do what you have always done, you're gonna get what you always got!" Kind of a simple way to think about it, but it does ring true.

As we discussed in Chapter One, Dr. Joe Dispenza tells us that regular humans have between 60,000 and 70,000 thoughts per day and 90 percent of them are the same as the day before. What this means is that our biology, our neurocircuitry, our neurochemistry, our hormones and even our gene expression, because it is based on how we think, feel and act, stays the same. We can change our programming, however, and reverse our repetitive behavior. Hypnotherapy is one way to accomplish this.

Using hypnotherapy to change your thoughts can lead to new thoughts, new feelings, new choices, new behaviors and new actions that in turn can inspire more new thoughts and break old cycles of thinking and behavior. All of these changes are accomplished without a pill, and with potentially lasting results.

It is estimated that as many as 70 percent or more of humans experience daily life under the influence of stress hormones, in survival mode and with a perception of danger, which triggers an almost perpetual fight or flight response. Remember when we discussed the fact that many people walk around in a state of hypnosis? This is what is at the root of the additional stress and fight or flight responses. Wouldn't it be better to be intentional about your trance and what you want to achieve instead of floating like a leaf on the current of a stream and going wherever the current takes you?

Let's finish up this chapter with a few notes on what a session is like. After what we call the cognitive interview, a question and answer period wherein I take a history of a client's issue and life experiences, I move them to a comfortable recliner and begin with a progressive relaxation exercise. Once relaxed, we move to an induction that brings the client into hypnosis. What is critical for the process to work is establishing rapport and trust. It is imperative to get the client relaxed and then overload them with what Dr. John Kappas, founder of Hypnosis and Motivation Institute (HMI), called message units. These units are really just bits of information or environmental stimuli so that we can trigger fight or flight and induce the escape mechanism that allows us to bypass the critical mind and gain access to the subconscious.

This does not mean it is an opportunity to "mess with someone's head." Remember, there is an inner awareness focus continuing without a complete escape from outer awareness. Also remember that there is never a loss of control. I have had some very intelligent people resist hypnotherapy because they didn't want me inside their thoughts and monkeying with their head! That's not how it works. Bypassing the critical mind is subtle and harmless, and it can be a pleasant experience as the client begins to float between the conscious and subconscious states.

Once the critical mind is bypassed I take the client through a couple of additional procedures we call deepeners Just like it sounds, these deepen the trance state. Then it is time for suggestions. These take the form of direct suggestions, metaphors and perhaps some imagery, all of which are in line with the client's experiences, their language patterns and worldview, and based upon the goals of the session. If you try to speak to a client in hypnosis with your words and don't consider their language patterns, it is not likely to be as effective. Before the induction you want to ask the client about colors, where in their body they feel things, their favorite place or places, perhaps someone they look up to or admire so that you can have them imagine getting advice from a visit with that person sitting on a bench in their favorite park. I once did a session on a cold rainy day and I had the client imagine being in a cabin in a cozy overstuffed chair next to a roaring fire. I was quite pleased with the image I conjured up only to be told by the client after the session that she hated mountain cabins and really wanted to be at the beach! I learned that lesson the hard way.

What is exceedingly important during any hypnotherapy session is to create imagery that supports the client's goals, allows them to visualize the desired outcome, and creates sensory engagement along the way. With younger clients you can get very creative with this process in order to make it successful. I had a twelve-year-old client who was struggling with performing a difficult move in her gymnastics program. I asked her what her favorite color was (green) and what her favorite animal was (dolphin), and then during hypnosis I asked her to envision riding upon the green dolphin and seeing herself flying on the green dolphin over the field where she was performing the difficult move and then seeing herself executing that move flawlessly. She loved the imagery and she later told me that she nailed the move just as she had seen herself do while in hypnosis.

So, that's just a small amount of what hypnotherapy is. Every client is different and so is every issue, and that is what makes hypnotherapy so interesting. Hypnotherapy has near universal application if done properly by someone trained and experienced. Training and experience are critical points in the hypnotherapy field as there are some who attempt to practice after a weekend seminar and don't really have a full understanding of the range of details necessary to be an effective hypnotherapist.

Academic research into hypnosis tends to identify two groups of participants; those who can be hypnotized and those who cannot, but I believe those who many in academia refer to as not hypnotizable are simply resisting, and with the proper preparation and willingness, everyone can be hypnotized. After years of practice, I believe the best training I received during my coursework was on counseling and interviewing. My greatest strength is my ability to get to the cause of the issue. As noted above, rarely is the cause what the client presents with, so there becomes a level of forensics involved in getting to the true cause. Without getting to the root cause of a client's concerns, you are just addressing symptoms and are not likely to see the lasting change that hypnotherapy has the potential to deliver. Hopefully this has been enough information to make you comfortable giving it a try!

CHAPTER FOUR

What Does Science Say?

What does science say about hypnosis and hypnotherapy? As mentioned earlier, many scientists and physicians give little credence to hypnotherapy because until recently it was defended only by case studies, histories, and anecdotal evidence. Moreover, I believe there may be lingering effects from the Mesmer controversy, perhaps even some residual reluctance left over from Dr. Sigmund Freud's departure from the modality and subsequent study and development of psychoanalysis.

Interestingly, there was a 2019 article in the American Journal of Clinical Hypnosis regarding "healing the rift" between hypnosis and psychoanalysis. The article noted that as Freud developed his own ideas, he abandoned the use of hypnosis and this change led to more than a century of disengagement between hypnosis and psychoanalysis characterized, with some exceptions, by mutual avoidance, dismissiveness, and incomplete appreciation of each by the other. In the past, there were challenges to the foundations of Freud's rationales and their dissemination. The article cited contemporary instances in which hypnosis and psychoanalysis are used together. The article also explored opportunities for mutual enrichment and enhancement. The judicious incorporation of insights and assets from each into the other was noted as long overdue.

Notwithstanding the article noted above, science, and medicine's short shrift of hypnotherapy was largely because medicine was taken in the direction of rational materialism, that is, measure, quantify and describe the component parts, structures and systems and if you cannot replicate this process through the scientific method, then it is not considered "evidence-based."

Science is generally understood and accepted to be the investigation of natural phenomena through observation, theoretical explanation, and experimentation, or the knowledge produced by such investigation. Science makes use of the scientific method, which includes the careful observation of natural phenomena, the formulation of a hypothesis, the conducting of one or more experiments to test the hypothesis, and the drawing of a conclusion that confirms or modifies the hypothesis. Simply stated, science is the emergence and development of systematic knowledge.

Humankind has always been inquisitive (well, at least since the formation of the neocortex as discussed in Chapter 3), needing to understand why things behave in a certain way, and trying to connect observation to prediction. Observation of the heavens is an example of this need to connect as we try to make sense of the seasonal changes in the position of the sun, moon and stars. The Mesopotamians, in about 4000 BCE, tried to explain their observations by suggesting that the Earth was at the center of the Universe, and that the other heavenly bodies moved around it. Much like hypnosis, that point became contentious and was finally settled, but not before much dispute and social implications. Nevertheless, humans have always been interested in the nature and origins of this Universe.

Astronomy wasn't the only early area of inquiry. The extraction of iron, which led to the Iron Age, is a chemical process that early metallurgists developed without understanding any of the science involved. They were still able to optimize the extraction by trial and error and learn from previous extraction attempts with copper and tin. Exactly how each of these processes was discovered is lost to time, but they were likely developed using observation and experimentation in a similar way to what scientists use today.

The early scientific method that led to observations of the seasons and heavenly predictions turned to metal development with the ancient Greeks. However, during the middle ages, science stagnated before dramatically reemerging in an Enlightenment period with scientific icons like Galileo Galilei and Isaac Newton in the 17th and 18th centuries. In this simplistic version of history, the long medieval hiatus of science and reason is often attributed to the influence of religion. The ensuing scientific revolution and the dominant march of science ever since are said to be the result of science managing to disentangle itself from the clutches of a censorial and deadening religious establishment.

There really was something quite remarkable and revolutionary about the new sciences of the 17th century. New experimental methods, new combinations of mathematics and physics, and revised understandings of nature and its meanings came to light along with the idea of science as a collective enterprise. Importantly, science was also aligned with a set of values to sustain it, and eventually propel it right into the center of Western culture (this center stage occupancy has had some interesting consequences that we will explore later). Science began to move away from being based on a confidence in the unaided powers of human reason and the senses. There was movement away from Aristotle's view that our cognitive and sensory powers were aligned with nature and would yield, without question, a relatively accurate picture of the world and its workings.

In medicine, too, the scientific method was embraced. There were some rather crude practices carried out by doctors in the 18th and 19th centuries, including bloodletting. There was even a medical device to actually blow smoke up your ass - no kidding - where do you think the phrase came from? It is generally accepted that our concept of medicine traces back to physician Hippocrates of Kos (460 – 370 BCE) who is considered the "father of modern medicine." The Hippocratic Corpus is a collection of early medical works from ancient Greece associated with Hippocrates and his students. Physicians take a Hippocratic Oath pledging adherence to a set of ethics.

During the Renaissance period, understanding of anatomy improved and the microscope was invented. The germ theory of disease in the nineteenth century led to cures for many infectious diseases. Military doctors advanced the methods of trauma treatment and surgery. Public health measures were developed, especially in the nineteenth century as the rapid growth of cities required systematic sanitary measures.

Advanced research centers opened in the early twentieth century and were often connected with major hospitals. The mid-twentieth century was also characterized by new biological treatments, such as antibiotics. These advancements, along with developments in chemistry, genetics, and lab technology, like the x-ray, led to what we view as modern medicine. Medicine was heavily professionalized in the twentieth century, and at the same time, disease specialization arose in the sense of providing medical care with respect to the specific characteristics of the disease as well as being provided by specialized medical professionals. The twenty-first century is often characterized by highly advanced research involving numerous fields of science as well as the mapping of the human genome.

The question arises, however, as to whether we have dehumanized health care. Have we become so complex and technical that we have lost our humanity? Are we disconnected from some of the organic and inherent capabilities that allowed us to survive and withstand a dangerous world with remarkable powers that defy technical description? As we rely on increasingly technical equipment and exceedingly complex explanations for health challenges faced by humans, have we abandoned amazing organic processes? Have we subjugated the mind to the brain and emphasized the mechanical and academic over the subtle and spiritual? A prime example of subtle unexplained esoteric phenomena that defies a mechanistic explanation is the remarkable placebo effect.

The placebo effect is well known and acknowledged by Western medicine. You know, fake treatments such as sugar pills, saline injections, and similar techniques. These techniques are routinely used in clinical trials as a control against which drugs, treatments, or surgeries are measured in order to determine if they are truly effective. In a landmark 1955 study by Dr. Henry Beecher featured in the Journal of the American Medical Association and titled The Powerful Placebo, about a third of people who were given inert ingredients like saltwater or sugar, for example, were not only cured in their minds, but also showed measurable physiological recovery. The placebo effect has been referred to as the doctor within.

In modern, evidence-based medicine, any drug, treatment, or surgery must do better than the placebo in trials in order to be deemed effective. So, the power of the placebo effect is not only acknowledged by evidenced-based medicine, it is used as a baseline determinant for what is considered an effective therapy. Yet it is discounted. This poses a practical problem for a doctor in modern practice. Dr. Deepak Chopra notes that the placebo effect is considered a nuisance to some modern doctors whose medical training preconditions them to consider drugs and surgery real medicine. Their medical ethics preclude prescribing fake drugs.

Dr. Chopra and others argue that the placebo effect is real medicine because it triggers the body's healing mechanism and it does so free from side effects. Every thought, decision, and action one engages in influences a chemical feedback loop within the body. For these reasons, it is critical to be aware of your self-talk and your thoughts. The placebo effect makes it very clear that expectation plays an incredibly important role in your healing and recovery. Expectation also plays a big role in hypnotherapy.

Conversely, just as you can positively influence your healing, you can damage your body's natural state of health or worsen your disease condition with negative thoughts. The fact that this input comes from the brain means that thoughts, moods, and expectations, detached as they may seem, can get translated into chemical messages just as surely as chemical therapies like drugs can. You must be responsible and deliberate in your thinking and in your self-interest to send positive messages to your cells as opposed to negative ones.

Expectancy plays a tremendous role in your day-to-day health, but it is especially powerful when you are sick and/or in a diseased state. It has been scientifically proven that focusing your attention on illness will make you sick. Ask any medical student if, after accumulating substantial knowledge about what can go wrong with the body and the endless ways in which the physical body can break down, they didn't at least once begin to experience physical symptoms. In fact, a 1966 study in the Journal of Medical Education titled Medical Students' Disease: Hypochondriasis in Medical Education found that 79 percent of students reported developing symptoms.

A more recent example can be seen in the response to the novel coronavirus outbreak in early 2020. Because of the repetitive news accounts highlighting authorities giving dire warnings (first requirement for hypnosis: authority), coupled with the latest symptoms, treatment and mortality rates broadcast in ongoing flash updates (second requirement for hypnosis: paradigm) people were afraid (third requirement: they felt something) and many people were convinced they had it when they did not, or were convinced that they had it in the months before even though authorities said that no one in the U. S. had it in December. These people became highly suggestable and could very well have even physically experienced the symptoms even if they did not, in fact, test positive for the virus.

This phenomenon has been referred to as the nocebo effect. Where the placebo effect reinforces the power of nurturing, hope, positive thinking, and expectation, the nocebo effect points to the power of negative thinking and how it can cause one to experience physical symptoms. In either case, we see the power of expectation, state of mind, and the foundation for the mind-body connection. This mind-body connection, its connection to expectation and self-healing are part of the elements within the mystery of hypnosis, as well as in humans' incredible capacity for self-healing.

Modern medicine acknowledges the placebo, but it tends to characterize it under the category of psychosomatic healing. Psychosomatic as a term is often heaped in with the likes of hypnosis, is generally believed to be "all in your head" and focused less on the healing aspect and more typically directed at the make yourself sick model which are characteristics of the nocebo state.

Psychosomatic medicine arose in the late eighteenth and early twentieth centuries in an effort to explain illnesses with no visible cause as well as what is referred to as spontaneous remission, or spontaneous healing. As noted, the term, Psychosomatic carries some baggage. There are associations with hypochondriasis and diseases that don't really exist, but the term was originally meant to encompass diseases of the body (soma) caused by the spirit, or the soul (psyche). Psychosomatic medicine was eventually developed to explain physical ills arising from underlying psychological disturbances.

Remember Bernheim's information transduction in suggestive therapeutics from Chapter 2, where ideas received are transformed into an act? It turns out that some of the most recent research attempting to explain the psychobiology of mind/body healing is looking at the limbic-hypothalamic system as a major mind-body information transducer. Moving beyond the simple correlation of stress as a suppression agent of the immune response, research is finding that mental experiences can be transduced into physiological responses characteristic of emotions in the limbic brain system.

For a long time, people thought of the brain and its partner, the central nervous system, much like the workings of an electrical system of communication. It was commonly believed that neurons, or nerve cells, form what could be compared to an old-fashioned landline telephone system with seemingly endless miles of complexly crisscrossing wiring. As scientists began to develop tools to help them move beyond the electrical brain and begin to see the chemical brain, science began to change, and with it, the popular understanding of brain chemistry and function.

As neuroscience developed and expanded along with the tools for understanding the chemical brain, we are better able to understand the mysterious processes at work in hypnosis and the placebo effect, and in mind-body healing. By the way, a whole new medical discipline has recently emerged called psychoneuroimmunology, which is just a fancy way of saying mind-body-spirit, but in a way that those who practice in evidence-based medicine can say with a straight face and clinical, scientific terminology.

Our expanded understanding is not all chemical. There are 12 cranial nerves in the body. They come in pairs and help to link the brain with other areas of the body, such as the head, neck, and torso. Some of these nerves send sensory information to the brain and are known to have sensory functions. Other cranial nerves control the movement of various muscles and the function of certain glands. These are known as motor functions. While some cranial nerves have either sensory or motor functions, others have both. The vagus nerve is such a nerve.

The word vagus, translated from Latin means wandering. This seems an appropriate name, as the vagus nerve is the longest cranial nerve. It runs all the way from the brain stem to part of the colon. The sensory functions of the vagus nerve are divided into two components: somatic components felt on the skin or in the muscles; and visceral components felt in the organs of the body. The vagus nerve represents the main component of the parasympathetic nervous system, which oversees a vast array of crucial bodily functions, including control of mood, immune response, digestion, and heart rate. It establishes one of the connections between the brain and the gastrointestinal tract and sends information about the state of the inner organs to the brain. It may very well be that the circuitry for transduction of information in mind-body healing is contained in the vagus nerve as the physical pathway for phenomena like a "gut feeling," or butterflies in the stomach, as well as the conduit for immune modulation from the brain to the organs.

Returning to the chemical system, we now see this system of chemical information as a second nervous system, and it has been shown to be more ancient and basic to the human organism. As it turns out, there were chemicals - peptides, for example, such as endorphins, being made inside cells long before there were neurons, and even before there were brains. As the knowledge grew and the research expanded, focus also expanded beyond the synapses and the synaptic gaps toward the neurotransmitters, the chemicals that jumped those gaps and facilitated information transduction (remember Bernheim and info becoming action!). Now, instead of the old electrical paradigm wherein a nerve was either turned on or turned off, we have a chemical paradigm with the chemicals giving information that can lead to such things as immune response, emotional reaction, even gene expression. That's right, even gene expression. The emerging science of epigenetics holds that we can modulate our gene expression when influenced by altered neurochemistry that often occurs with mind-body tactics like meditation, mindfulness and hypnotherapy.

The central dogma of modern medicine, molecular biology, is giving way to a new paradigm in which it is understood that your DNA is not your destiny. In other words, instead of set at birth, your genetic material can change. And it is believed that through focused concentration we can affect the circumstances under which we can consciously alter how our DNA shows up.

Science moved toward rationalism, materialism and the thinking of the modern age in the seventeenth century away from emotion and the ancient link between emotion and health. But now, it might be argued and supported by the latest research that there is a clear link between health and the science of emotions and consciousness bringing us full circle in the emotion/science/emotion continuum of human health.

The modern practice of medicine with its narrow focus characterized by highly segmented specialization and overemphasis on technology to the exclusion of the personal touch is a toxic mix often seen as cold, calculating and technical with paternalistic interaction. Modern medicine uses overly clinical and technical jargon that ultimately disconnects people from their body and their health care. The disillusionment of regular people over the disconnected, overly-complex and complicated, dehumanized practice of modern medicine has created a call for alternative options beyond the narrowmindedness of modern scientific thinking. And this desire for alternative approaches to health-care comes at an exciting time as we become able to explain what is going on in the physical body during mind-body therapies and exercises.

We have come to understand what the molecules of emotion are and how inter-organ communication facilitates the intelligence of our own bodies. This inter-organ communication can be an agent of the immune system, as demonstrated by the vagus nerve. This agency can take the form of positive self-healing, as in the case of the placebo effect as well as positive mind-body modalities like hypnotherapy, or in negative impacts like the nocebo effect where we can literally make ourselves sick. In either case, we have more control over our health than we previously understood, and science is backing it up. Moreover, we have reached a place where we can finally explain what is going on in hypnosis and other mind-body modalities.

Just as science is coming full circle, it's getting even more fun and exciting. As we move beyond the atomic level of composition, past the photon, neutron and electron into the quantum field and the realm of neutrinos, quarks, muons and gluons, things are getting really interesting. In fact, quantum mechanics is more like the mystical beliefs and observations of ancient societies than the materialism of Newtonian mechanics. Non-local interaction, the observer effect and other features of the quantum field seem pretty magical. But that is a topic for another book. For now, let's return to what science has to say about hypnotherapy.

Dr. David Spiegel is Associate Chair of Psychiatry & Behavioral Sciences and Medical Director of the Center for Integrative Medicine at Stanford University School of Medicine. Since 1975, Dr. Spiegel has been at the forefront of research exploring the simple question: what's going on in the brain when you're hypnotized? For some people, hypnosis is associated with loss of control or stage tricks, or the Hollywood representation noted previously. But doctors like Spiegel know hypnosis is a serious science that reveals the brain's ability to heal medical and psychiatric conditions.

"Hypnosis is the oldest Western form of psychotherapy, but it's been tarred with the brush of dangling watches and purple capes," Spiegel has stated. "In fact, it's a very powerful means of changing the way we use our minds to control perception, and our bodies."

Spiegel has stated further that hypnotherapy is the ultimate therapeutic partnership, a relationship that forms between a patient and clinician that empowers the patient to take ownership of their own healing. In this partnership, healing can be fully realized when patients become active participants in the development of their therapeutic plan. As an active participant, people feel in control of their own health and are more likely to make sustained lifestyle changes that will lead to improved health.

Some of Spiegel's recent research has demonstrated a drop in activity in the dorsal anterior cingulate, part of the salience network of the brain, a context decoder, or in layperson terms - a part of the brain that alerts you to what you should pay attention to and what you can ignore. This part of the brain, which fires up when there's something to worry about, actually calms down during hypnosis. A second change was observed in the dorsolateral prefrontal cortex, the part of the brain where you plan things and carry out routines, and the insula, a part of the brain that helps regulate body functions. These two parts of the brain began syncing up in their connectivity, like altering blood pressure and heart rate. This suggests that during hypnosis the brain intensifies its connection to the body. We can see evidence of this when the hypnotized individual experiences a slower heart rate and rhythmic breathing with a likely corresponding decrease in blood pressure.

At the same time, other areas of the brain become less connected during hypnosis. The researchers saw more of a disconnect between the same region of planning and routines, the dorsolateral prefrontal cortex, and a part of the brain characterized by self-reflection. In hypnosis people tend to do things without reflection. As a result, people will sometimes do embarrassing or silly things in staged hypnosis shows. They are not thinking about it, they're just doing it.

Taken together, these changes help explain how hypnosis can have powerful effects, including reducing stress, anxiety, pain and self-consciousness. Spiegel's previous research has shown that when people in pain are taught self-hypnosis, they had half the pain and used half the pain medication compared to those who were just given access to opioids. Based upon his research as well as his own clinical experience, Spiegel believes hypnotherapy should be used instead of painkillers in many cases. Just think of the applications! Could teaching patients self-hypnosis reduce the opioid addiction problem we have in this country?

Irving Kirsch, a lecturer and director of the Program in Placebo Studies at Harvard Medical School says hypnosis is a well-studied and legitimate form of adjunct treatment for conditions ranging from obesity and pain after surgery to anxiety and stress.

In two other studies, hypnosis buffered the effects of stress on immune functions in medical students at exam time, and the comparison of self-hypnosis with and without immune imagery confirmed advantages to targeted imagery for both immune function and mood, and importantly, fewer winter viral infections. The implications for health were investigated in a third study in patients with virulent and chronic herpes simplex virus. Six weeks of training almost halved recurrence, improved mood, and reduced levels of clinical depression and anxiety. Immune functions were up-regulated, notably functional natural killer cell activity to HSV-1.

New replicable evidence has been reviewed on the importance of cognitive activation, a personality difference whose neurophysiological underpinning is consistent with left hemispheric preferential influences over the immune system. Now that the validation of psychological interventions includes advantages for health, researchers believe hypnosis, which had been characterized by modest, small scale, largely preliminary studies, warrants a greater investment in research.

Further, a meta-analysis of 18 studies revealed a moderate to large hypnoanalgesic effect, supporting the efficacy of hypnotic techniques for pain management. The results also indicated that hypnotic suggestion was equally effective in reducing both clinical and experimental pain. The overall results suggest broader application of hypnoanalgesic techniques with pain patients, as well as the observation that hypnosis interventions consistently produce significant decreases in pain associated with a variety of chronic-pain problems. Hypnosis was generally found to be more effective than non-hypnotic interventions such as attention, physical therapy, and education.

Perhaps the most credible scientific explanation yet comes from a study/article titled, Brain Activity and Functional Connectivity Associated with Hypnosis, by authors Heidi Jiang, Matthew P. White, Michael D. Greicius, Lynn C. Waelde and David Spiegel, in the publication Cerebral Cortex (2017). The authors state in the abstract: "(H)ypnosis has proven clinical utility, yet changes in brain activity underlying the hypnotic state have not yet been fully identified. Previous research suggests that hypnosis is associated with decreased default mode network (DMN) activity and that high hypnotizability is associated with greater functional connectivity between the executive control network (ECN) and the salience network (SN). We used functional magnetic resonance imaging (MRI) to investigate activity and functional connectivity among these three networks in hypnosis. We selected 57 of 545 healthy subjects with very high or low hypnotizability using two hypnotizability scales. All subjects underwent four conditions in the scanner: rest, memory retrieval, and two different hypnosis experiences guided by standard pre-recorded instructions in counterbalanced order. Seeds for the ECN, SN, and DMN were left and right dorsolateral prefrontal cortex, dorsal anterior cingulate cortex (dACC), and posterior cingulate cortex (PCC), respectively. During hypnosis there was reduced activity in the dACC, increased functional connectivity between the dorsolateral prefrontal cortex (DLPFC;ECN) and the insula in the SN, and reduced connectivity between the ECN (DLPFC) and the DMN (PCC). These changes in neural activity underlie the focused attention, enhanced somatic and emotional control, and lack of self-consciousness that characterizes hypnosis."

The foregoing is hardly an exhaustive account of what science says about hypnosis and hypnotherapy. And my apologies if the terms and references were difficult to understand and follow, I wanted you to see what the study said and how those who are studying hypnosis scientifically are talking about it and utilizing it as well as what their scientific methods were/are. These are the terms for the pathways in our brain that control behavior and thinking and understanding how hypnosis affects them is an important piece. But you don't need to know what the insula of the salient network is, or the dorsolateral prefrontal cortex, but realize that real science is being done and hypnotherapy is part of real physiological activity and not just part of Mesmer's personality!

Nor is it a complete account of science and its modern manifestation. Inasmuch as I have tried to give a representation, a flavor if you will, for what science has come to in its ever pressing forward march to explain, objectify and describe the phenomenon and modality of hypnosis, it is a faithful representation.

Now let's move on to a description of some of the uses of hypnosis and a discussion of its application articulated in a number of recent studies.

CHAPTER FIVE

What Is Hypnotherapy Good For?

The range of issues to which hypnotherapy can be successfully applied runs the gamut of human experience. I know, you're probably thinking panacea, nothing can help with everything. Because hypnosis is a technique that utilizes the client's own inner world, and a skillful hypnotherapist trained in counseling and interviewing can get to the original programming that led a person into the issue in the first place, it really can be deployed for the gamut of human situations. In the following pages I will detail some of the more common areas of application for hypnotherapy and cover various studies and their results from the evidence-based community.

Research continues to expand into various areas of healthcare and the application of hypnotherapy continues to be applied in beneficial ways. A recent search of scholar.google.com, a search engine with a focus on peer-reviewed scientific journals and academic textbooks, revealed more than 15,000 peer-reviewed studies, text references and academic articles related to hypnotherapy. A report by the National Institutes of Health (NIH), for example, cites evidence supporting the efficacy of hypnosis for relief of chronic pain in cancer, irritable bowel syndrome, and tension headaches. In the cancer setting, hypnotherapy is used to reduce stress and anxiety, both conditions ever-present after a cancer diagnosis, and typically throughout the recovery and healing process. The resolution is that through hypnotherapy, one can turn off the stress response and activate the relaxation response, which is where healing takes place. Beyond anxiety and stress reduction, hypnotherapy is also effective in facilitating therapeutic imagery journeys where the client visualizes healing. Also, hypnotherapy can be effective at releasing repressed emotions that many cancer clients tend to hold onto that complicate healing.

In addition to the growing body of evidence of the non-invasive power of hypnotherapy in the medical setting, there are the well-accepted applications of using hypnotherapy for behavioral change such as smoking cessation, weight loss, sports performance, test preparation and other habit control measures. Many people have utilized hypnotherapy to reach goals and to create positive change in their life because it works. In an era when chemical therapy is too often a first resort and we can be too quick to reach for a pill, which in some cases has side effects that require a second pill, hypnotherapy poses a process in which client and practitioner can work together using natural processes for health and betterment.

In a study conducted in 2015 that included 150 participants, a researcher and nurse at the City of Hope Cancer Center found that 78% of those who used hypnosis experienced significant, lasting reduction in symptoms such as anxiety, pain, sleeplessness, fatigue, nausea and vomiting. In an article entitled "Hypnosis for Cancer Care: Over 200 Years Young" in a journal for clinicians, the authors noted that "Hypnosis has been used to provide psychological and physical comfort to individuals diagnosed with cancer for nearly 200 years." The stated goals of the review were: 1) to describe hypnosis and its components and to dispel misconceptions; 2) to provide an overview of hypnosis as a cancer prevention and control technique (covering its use in weight management, smoking cessation, as an adjunct to diagnostic and treatment procedures, survivorship, and metastatic disease); and 3) to discuss future research directions. Overall, the literature supports the benefits of hypnosis for improving quality of life during the course of cancer and its treatment."

Perhaps the area of greatest value from hypnotherapy is behavioral change. As explained, from the time we are born until about the age of ten we are in a relative state of hypnosis, highly suggestable to the people in our most immediate sphere of influence. Our subconscious is forming and as we gather our experiences, they are stored and labeled as known. These experiences are a collection of good and bad: you like birthday parties, chocolate cake and hugs from your mom; but you don't like spankings or broccoli or getting up early in the morning. Good, or bad, the experiences are lumped into your knowns and become part of your programming, pleasure seeking and pain avoiding. Sometimes even the bad things are deemed okay because they are known. The subconscious loves the known and is afraid of the unknown. This is why people stay in situations that are terrible for them, leaving the situation presents the unknown which is far scarier than the known, even if the unknown is bad for them.

So, too, does the dialogue of those around you become part of your programming. For instance, examples of the phrases repeatedly said by those around you like, "Money doesn't grow on trees"; "Why can't you be more like your brother?" "You will never live up to your potential." These statements are ingrained into our subconscious and just like the placebo/nocebo effect, your self-talk will reflect these notions and you will live them out.

In hypnotherapy the critical mind is bypassed and the subconscious is spoken to directly in order to undo some of this programming utilizing tools like metaphor and imagery. Often I do inner child work and mild regression-to-cause as I take clients back to meet that little kid who was so impressionable and have the adult client reassure their inner child that they always did their best and that they love them and can visit whenever they want. This is facilitated by having the client, while in cataleptic hypnosis, travel back in time in their mind. The client is given suggestions to remember details of their childhood home, toys, books, events, people and other details to fully engage their imagination and give them a sense of really being there through detailed imagery.

When they have gone back in time, in their mind, I might have them signal me with what we refer to as an ideomotor response, that is, lift a finger for yes as an example, to let me know they are there and engaged with their inner child. This engages the body with the subconscious mind and makes it realistic. The client can imagine giving their younger self love and affection that they might feel they did not get, or reassurances and recognition. And the suggestion that they can meet and visit anytime preconditions the client to be able to receive information from their higher self in terms of any unresolved issues that remain.

You may engage in behavior that you cannot change no matter how determined you are, or how hard you have tried. This is likely because the pattern originated from an experience in childhood. Other times behavior is established later in life as a result of social acceptance, peer pressure or other powerful influences that lead to our subconscious mind accepting the behavior as a known. Other times behavior can develop as a reflex, or a defense mechanism. No matter what the origin of unwanted behavior, hypnotherapy is a great way to make positive change.

Taking it a step further, many clients present with seemingly clear-cut symptoms such as excess weight, a smoking addiction, sleeplessness, pain, headache or ulcers. It is tempting to focus solely on the symptoms, develop a hypnotherapy action plan, and formulate action goals in terms of alleviating symptoms only. Experience has taught me, however, that if cause is what we want to get to in order to make lasting change, a comprehensive evaluation of the client that includes a detailed history as well as an assessment of the presenting behavioral complaint is absolutely necessary. One objective of this assessment is to determine the nature of the behavioral development and the client's coping resources.

If a practitioner takes the time necessary and applies artful interviewing techniques when taking a client's history and has established a rapport, then it follows that the cause of the behavioral and health related symptoms will emerge and unfold. Drilling down beyond the anecdotes listed above, there are a number of areas that can produce behavioral issues as well as health related issues.

Causative factors include predisposing biological factors such as genetic predisposition, developmental/situational influences such as early nutritional patterns, tissue damage through infection, acquired drug sensitivity, acute injury, extreme physical inactivity as well as hormonal changes associated with menstruation and pregnancy. Psychosocial and stress factors like stressful life events, daily hassles, environmental factors such as noise pollution, exposure to extreme temperatures, barometric, weather and altitude changes, exposure to toxic substances, radiation, toxic foodstuffs, social environment isolation, overcrowding. Also included among causative factors are personality traits, such as type A behavior, inadequate coping resources, lifestyle factors, chronic physical inactivity, diet and behavioral excesses like smoking and problematic eating as well as substance abuse.

Maintenance factors that can lead to health and behavioral issues include secondary conditioning, anticipatory anxiety and panic, adoption of illness behaviors, overuse of treatment - especially medications, addictive behavior; attempts to prevent withdrawal, maladaptive cognitions, negative self-statements, lack of self-efficacy, body image and self-image problems, conflict, intrapsychic systemic issues (family, health provider), social influence, persuasion, and negative modeling. Even advertising reinforcing lifestyle influences can be a maintenance factor. If unresolved, these factors can lead to behavioral issues and even become somatized into the body and manifest as illness.

It is almost never what the client comes in for that is the real issue they need to address, and to get to lasting change, it is extremely important to get to the underlying cause of the issue with each client.

Stress is another area where hypnotherapy has a proven track record of effectively helping clients. The very pathway into hypnosis is through deep relaxation, often utilizing a progressive relaxation of the body to induce trance. D. Corydon Hammond notes in a study detailed in the Journal Expert Review of Neurotherapeutics titled Hypnosis in the Treatment of Anxiety- and Stress-Related Disorders that there is a "tremendous volume of research (that) provides compelling evidence that hypnosis is an efficacious treatment for state anxiety (e.g., [the state of the mind in a situation like] prior to tests, surgery and medical procedures) and anxiety-related disorders such as headaches and irritable bowel syndrome."

I have had stressed out clients come in for regular hypnotherapy visits because it was the only time in their busy lives, they actually felt relaxed. From the perspective of the person being hypnotized, and I speak from experience, a 50-minute session of hypnotherapy can feel like a two or even three-hour nap. Given estimates that more than 70 percent of people today routinely experience the stress response, often for sustained periods, a modality such as hypnotherapy could mean the difference between stress management and dis-ease. One study determined that long-term stress suppresses or dysregulates innate and adaptive immune responses by altering the cytokine balance, inducing low-grade chronic inflammation and suppressing numbers, trafficking, and function of immunoprotective cells. Chronic stress may also increase susceptibility to some types of cancer by suppressing cytokines and protective T cells and increasing regulatory/suppressor T cell function. At present, one of the aggravating symptoms of COVID-19 is a cytokine storm that attacks the lungs and can in the extreme suffocate the sufferer. Hypnotherapy could be a powerful tool in the overall approach to the stress, anxiety and symptoms of our current major health threat if deployed appropriately.

Anxiety is another area where hypnotherapy has a high responsive rate. A 2018 meta-analysis that quantified the effectiveness of hypnosis in treating anxiety found at the end of active treatment, a mean weighted effect for the average participant receiving hypnosis was reduced anxiety more at a level greater than 79% of control participants who did not receive hypnosis. At the longest follow-up, seven trials yielded a mean weighted effect size demonstrating the average participant treated with hypnosis improved more than 84% of control participants who did not receive hypnosis.

Again, the relaxation component coupled with reframing and imagery are key benefits of the modality. I often give the client an anchor, a small movement they can perform discreetly that allows them to revivify the relaxation of hypnotherapy. Helping clients understand that anticipation is often a trigger allows them to recognize and deploy tools before the anxiety builds to a level that becomes a problem.

In simplest terms, and with an Eastern perspective, anxiety is living in the future and depression is living in the past. The goal is to remain present, which is a gift, that's why they call it the present. And while these points are important for clients to understand, often they come in after having suffered through symptoms for a sustained period of time and after trying chemical therapies that were either ineffective, had undesirable side effects, or both. Depression is an awful condition, and because it has a psychological ideation (origin), I have to obtain a referral from a physician or psychologist in order to see a client formally diagnosed with depression. Once that is in place, hypnotherapy can really help turn things around. I know it did for me, which is one of the primary reasons I sought to study hypnotherapy.

For me, when I was in the depths of despair during my cancer journey and it had returned requiring a second round of radiation that was exacerbated by aggravating factors in other areas of my life, a reframe of my situation and a hypnotic anchoring of that reframe gave me considerable relief. Another example is a client, Jaime, who was completely depressed over an impossible situation with her husband, mother in law and sister in law, that she saw no way of resolving. Reframing the situation, establishing cognitively and in hypnosis discrete actions she could take to give life to the reframe and having her begin by creating boundaries and leading by example and then visualizing it happen in hypnosis first, feeling the empowerment in her body that would follow - while in hypnosis - allowed her to break free from her feelings of despair and hopelessness. Going inward, changing herself and her thinking first led the conflict to dissolve and left the others asking what happened to you? You changed. And rather than need credit, or point fingers, she just smiled because that is what we preconditioned her to do when her reasonable actions turned the heat down on the situation.

In a meta study published in 2019 a hypnotic intervention for depression was compared with a control condition in reducing depression symptoms. Ten studies incorporating 13 trials of hypnosis that met the inclusion criteria results indicated that the average participant receiving hypnosis showed more improvement than about 76% of control participants. It was noted that these results are comparable to those associated with well-known psychological interventions for depression (like cognitive therapy and interpersonal therapy) and suggest hypnosis is a highly effective way of alleviating the symptoms of depression. The analysis went on to suggest that clinicians may wish to give serious consideration to hypnosis as a treatment option when working with clients and patients who are depressed.

I often teach my clients to meditate and to practice mindfulness. The mind is a powerful asset and you can either be its master or its slave. The path to mastery is paved with the techniques of quiet and stillness. Most clients respond initially with, "There's no way I can clear my mind." This is a statement I am quite familiar with. I was an analyst and my overactive, analytical mind served me very well during a 25 year career in politics, but it can also be your worst enemy and can even make you sick if you do not learn to be its master. Just deciding to be quiet and still every day at the same time (I always recommend first thing in the morning before life gets in the way) is a huge step. Critical to this working is the daily part. Once in a routine you can focus on your breathing or use ear buds and a YouTube selection, there are thousands available and finding what appeals to you is part of the fun. Also, a good book to start with is *How to Meditate: A Practical Guide,* by Kathleen McDonald, or *Out of Your Mind,* by Alan Watts.

Trauma is defined as a deeply distressing or disturbing experience. In general, trauma can be defined as a psychological, emotional response to an event or an experience that is deeply distressing or disturbing. While trauma is a universally understood term, everyone processes a traumatic event differently because we all face them through the subjective lens of our own prior experiences.

When I was in the middle of my cancer journey, after the second round of radiation and having my situation compounded by my health crisis causing difficulties in my marriage (everyone copes with stress in their own way) I wasn't sleeping. I was fearful of losing my life, my family and all of the material things I had worked so hard for. My physician, the guy who had so adeptly diagnosed my cancer early, said I had post traumatic stress disorder (PTSD). He prescribed pills that had thoughts of suicide listed among the many side effects. I told him that what I was experiencing was definitely traumatic, that any reasonable person experiencing what I was experiencing would experience trauma, but that in no way did I have a disorder - the D part of PTSD. I explained to him that I was fighting for my life and there was no way I was taking a pill that might make me want to kill myself.

I utilized hypnotherapy to re-frame my situation and after a great deal of work with an amazing practitioner I was able to come to see the experience differently. But when I was in the middle of the acute effects of trauma and heightened stress, anxiety and depression that accompanied the set of overwhelming circumstances, there was no way I was going to heal from the invasive surgeries, the radiation therapies and the accompanying unforeseen personal issues that I faced.

Trauma is cumulative, which means each trauma builds upon the last and compounds the effects. Unless you resolve the repressed emotions associated with the trauma they will fester and create unforeseen issues in your daily life. These issues may not surface right away, lying dormant until at some point they emerge in the form of health or behavioral issues. When these issues do arise, the time interval between the traumatic event and the resulting issue hides the causal connection and makes it difficult to associate the issue with the underlying trauma.

Often, shock and denial are typical reactions to a traumatic event. Over time, these emotional responses may fade, but a survivor may also experience reactions long-term. These can include unpredictable emotions, anger, flashbacks and persistent feelings of sadness and despair. Physical symptoms can include intense feelings of guilt, nausea and headaches, a feeling of responsibility for the event, feelings of isolation and hopelessness, and an altered sense of shame.

And trauma doesn't always take the form of an overwhelming distressing moment or experience, it can be something subtle like a very embarrassing moment, a slight, or a bitter disappointment. I had a client named Bob who was a union camera operator for 30 years in television and movies. He was diagnosed with a rare blood cancer and was struggling with the many medications he had to take and how they made him feel. Like most cancer clients, he also faced some fear.

When Bob first came in, we spent a great deal of time going over his history and experiences. Up to this point, his life had been great, and after much thought, he could not come up with a painful, deep emotional or traumatic experience from his life. I found it hard to believe, but I didn't tell him that.

I decided to approach things with Bob differently. I asked if he had ever had a bitter disappointment. He thought for a moment, and then the light went on. He then proceeded to share with me that despite an illustrious career replete with union leadership roles, he had been on a set and the producer was very hands-on and took over his camera. It had been a long day, and they were shooting long into the night. With nothing to do because his camera had been taken over, he fell asleep.

When he was found sleeping, it didn't matter that someone else was working the camera, he was fired. He felt deeply ashamed and embarrassed. So ashamed and embarrassed he took an early retirement, and despite still loving his career, what he'd done his entire adult life, he put himself out to pasture. Working through this disappointment allowed Bob to release these repressed emotions, and his health improved.

A 2013 European study noted that clinical reports and observations going back almost two centuries consistently indicate that hypnotherapy is an effective modality for the treatment of post-traumatic stress disorder (PTSD). Pierre Janet was the first clinician to describe the successful application of hypnotic techniques in PTSD symptom reduction. Hypnotherapy may accelerate the formation of a therapeutic alliance (rapport) and contribute to a positive treatment outcome. Hypnotic techniques may be valuable for symptoms such as anxiety, widespread pain complaints, dissociation, and sleep disturbances. Hypnotic techniques may also facilitate the grueling tasks of working through traumatic memories, increasing coping skills, and promoting a sense of competency.

I am certified in hypnotherapy for PTSD, but sadly, it is not widely known how effective hypnotherapy is with respect to trauma, so few people take advantage of it. I hope that will change.

Remember the discussion above about the placebo/nocebo effects? Where you can literally make yourself sick or better based upon your thinking? Well, disease, or dis-ease can sometimes result from our thoughts and lifestyle, from unresolved emotional wounds and traumas. The evidence-based health community calls this somatization, when we push the pain of unresolved emotions into our body.

This phenomenon is known as somatic symptom disorder (SSD formerly known as "somatization disorder" or "somatoform disorder"). It is a form of mental illness that causes one or more bodily symptoms, including pain. The symptoms can involve one or more different organs and body systems, such as: pain, neurologic problems, autoimmune symptoms and gastrointestinal complaints. There are several areas of SSD and include somatization disorder, undifferentiated somatoform disorder, hypochondriasis, conversion disorder, pain disorder, body dysmorphic disorder, and somatoform disorder not otherwise specified. Think of it as updated psychosomatic health related issues.

A 2007 European meta-analysis was conducted with 21 randomized, controlled clinical studies to evaluate efficacy of hypnosis in psychosomatic disorders. Studies compared patients exclusively treated with hypnotherapy to untreated controls. The meta-analysis clearly indicated hypnotherapy is highly effective in treatment of psychosomatic disorders.

The imagery deployed in hypnotherapy is very powerful. I am certified in hypnotherapy for pre-surgery and post-surgery. There are several studies that show the effectiveness of hypnotherapy in both pre-surgical and post-surgical settings and it is not difficult to understand why if you take a moment to look at what we do. I start by having the client visualize their body cooperating with the healing process, with trusting and cooperating with their amazing team of highly trained healing professionals who will be utilizing their years of vast experience and training to do their very best to help them heal. The imagery progresses to become even more detailed regarding visualizing the body cooperating, and then we precondition them to post-surgical healing with reduced pain and an expedited healing window. I helped a client with a difficult arthroscopic procedure for removal of a colostomy bag and reconnection of the healed intestine. The client told me after the procedure the doctor asked what he had done to prepare because everything went so much smoother than anticipated. Further, just as we had visualized in his hypnosis, there was less pain and an attenuated healing period. This also meant less reliance on pain medication.

I literally could go on, and on about the many benefits of hypnotherapy. The volumes of studies and papers tell a compelling story. But we will stop here with the health-related applications of hypnotherapy and turn briefly to the better-known areas that hypnotherapy is good for, namely, motivation and self-improvement.

As we have discussed, hypnotherapy can help us break the programming of old subconscious thinking habits that prevent us from making progress. Some of these programmed habits have names like fear of failure, being overly critical, or lacking confidence. Hypnotherapy can retrain the subconscious to stop these harmful habits and re-frame them in a more positive direction.

Even if you're not a procrastinator, maybe you just don't feel the motivation, drive and ambition to reach your goals;

hypnotherapy can help you, too. Like procrastination, a lack of motivation is caused by programmed subconscious thinking. We might avoid a particular task because we're overwhelmed, or we're focused on how unpleasant the task will be, or the thing was cast in a negative light by someone in our sphere of influence when we were young.

It is likely that we've trained our subconscious not to be a positive, encouraging supporter of our own endeavors. Instead, the subconscious, that inner voice in our heads, the keeper of our self-talk, becomes a bad influence, a detractor, telling us that we shouldn't even try.

That's where hypnotherapy becomes very useful. Using hypnotherapy, we can directly influence how the mind responds to adversity and transform it into a powerful ally, your cheerleader, motivating and encouraging you to forge ahead. Not feeling motivated doesn't just affect small tasks, it affects work and relationships and, if left unaddressed, it can cause depression and anxiety over time. This is when a lack of motivation becomes problematic and exponentially more than just a question of motivation. At the very least, when lack of motivation tendencies are left unattended, they can develop into chronic motivation troubles. When you lack motivation, you might notice yourself losing interest in subjects fast; procrastinating; failing to finish tasks; losing track of goals and objectives; feeling like you could be accomplishing more; or worse, feeling depressed, anxious or gloomy.

A lack of drive is often caused by habitual negative thinking. We've trained the mind to think about a particular task in a certain way and avoid doing it. There are numerous reasons a lack of motivation keeps us from reaching goals. For some, it's a fear of failure. The idea of not being good is too much, and the subconscious has been trained to persuade us to avoid it. Or, it might be the opposite: a fear of success. The subconscious has spent so much time feeling unfulfilled that it has become comfortable since living without success is the known, and attaining success is the scary unknown. There are numerous reasons we don't pursue our goals. A few common reasons you will recognize as the usual suspects include: feeling overwhelmed - I often tell clients that you eat an elephant one bite at a time; negative self-talk - often the voice from your childhood; people pleasing - the martyr's excuse; lack of interest; lack of confidence; focusing on the unpleasantness; and procrastination.

These are just some of the common reasons we lack motivation. There are more. In fact, many external factors like depression, anxiety and stress are also reasons we avoid getting things done. All are influenced by past experiences, attitudes, beliefs and adaptation. We've trained our subconscious to respond negatively and to put things off and avoid the hard or unpleasant tasks. Hypnotherapy is a powerful tool for releasing those unhelpful automatic responses and replacing them with a response that motivates and drives you into action. One reason hypnosis is so effective is that it allows us to work directly with the subconscious mind. In hypnosis, we relax the mind and body and arrive at a hyper focused, deeply relaxed state. As we discussed, it's similar to meditation or daydreaming. In this state we can speak directly to the subconscious and provide it with helpful suggestions. These carefully worded suggestions can then help empower the subconscious to change and unseat some of those harmful patterns that have unconsciously come to control our lives.

Hypnotherapy can help you want to achieve success serving as a powerful motivator. Hypnotherapy can also help you feel personal responsibility to get things done and reestablish a sense of drive, a powerful tool for keeping us motivated. The goal is to help reprogram the subconscious' natural, automatic responses through more positive ways of dealing with issues. If we envision success and even expect it, we are much more likely to achieve success and stay motivated. Through hypnosis, we can reprogram the subconscious to be a powerful ally, encouraging and helping us believe in our abilities. Research backs up these approaches.

A 2012 study, for example, examined how hypnotherapy could help people with anxiety overcome procrastination. After undergoing hypnotherapy, the participants reported lower procrastination scores, which suggests that hypnosis can improve motivation. Another study of college students found that hypnosis could help roughly half of them overcome procrastination. And there are other studies that show hypnotherapy can alter our perception about tasks and subjects, i.e. helping us overcome perceptions of a task being overwhelming or impossible, and improve our focus, as well. The ability to focus on a single task can help motivate us to achieve tasks and reach our goals.

Hypnotherapy can be used to improve any area of life. As we covered in the preceding pages, it is most commonly used to lose weight, quit smoking, sleep better and generally relieve stress, but it has also been found equally useful to increase productivity and concentration, improve confidence and self-esteem, enhance relationships and ease childbirth. The website of the nationally accredited Hypnosis Motivation Institute (HMI) where I was trained, has a list of 145 issues that hypnotherapy can be used to help with, from abandonment to writer's block and a whole world in between. This list can be found at hypnosis.edu/help.

The Center for Success notes that many famous people have used hypnotherapy over the years. *Included in this group are athletes who have used hypnotherapy for success:*

- Steve Hooker of Australia won the 2008 Gold Medal in Pole Vaulting after his hypnotist helped him visualize his success.
- In 2012, Felix Baumgartner became the first person to reach supersonic speed without traveling in a jet or a spacecraft after hopping out of a capsule that had reached an altitude of 128,100 feet above the Earth.
- 2008: The only two shooters who won gold medals for the U.S. worked with a hypnotherapist.
- 1984: Mary Lou Retton used hypnosis to block pain in her foot and won the Gold Medal for gymnastics.
- 1983: The Chicago White Sox hired a full-time hypnotist and made the playoffs.
- 1967: The Swiss Ski Team used a hypnotherapist and three members won medals.
- At the age of 13, Tiger Woods began seeing a hypnotist to help him to block out distractions and focus on the golf course.
- Jimmy Connors is said to have used hypnosis techniques

to practice his winning strokes prior to the US Open Championship.

- Kevin McBride, the celebrated Irish heavyweight boxing champion summons his hypnotist before every game to get into the right frame of mind.
- Championship golfer Jack Nicklaus lauded hypnotherapy and visualization techniques as the sole reason for his improved concentration.

Celebrities who have used hypnotherapy for weight loss:
- Orlando Bloom was so hooked on chocolate as a child that his mother called in a hypnotist to help him shape up.
- Fergie, the lead singer of the Black Eyed Peas, keeps a hypnotherapist on speed dial when she's touring, according to Marie Claire magazine.
- Lily Allen (singer)
- Sarah Ferguson, Duchess of York (former member of the British Royal family)
- Sophie Dahl (model)
- Geri Halliwell (singer)
- Chuck Clausen (former coach of the Philadelphia Eagles)
- Celebrities who have used hypnotherapy for stuttering or fear of speaking in public:
- Bruce Willis had stuttering problems throughout his youth and was always scared it would affect his acting career. He used hypnotherapy and overcame it.
- Tiger Woods had stuttering problems in childhood, but he overcame them through hard work and practice and hypnotherapy.

- Julia Roberts admitted the fact that she stuttered when she was younger, but she now speaks fluidly and is a respected actress.
- Mel Tillis' stutter developed during his childhood, a result of a bout of malaria.

Famous people who have used hypnotherapy for career success:
- Carl Jung and Sigmund Freud developed modern psychiatry as a result of learning about and practicing hypnosis.
- Mozart (1756-91) apparently composed a famous opera while hypnotized.
- Albert Einstein (1879-1955) physicist – was known to go into a trance through self-hypnosis every afternoon. His theory of relativity came to him during one of these sessions. He also used trance states to develop his ideas.
- Lord Alfred Tennyson (1809-92) wrote complete poems while hypnotized.
- Thomas Edison used self-hypnosis on a regular basis.
- Aldous Huxley used trance-like states to explore the nature of consciousness.
- Rachmaninov (1873-1943) reputedly composed one of his concertos following a post-hypnotic suggestion.
- Sir Winston Churchill used post-hypnotic suggestions in order to stay awake and carry out his duties as Prime Minister during WWII.

Famous athletes who used hypnotherapy for performance:
- Boxers Ingmar Johannson, Ken Norton, Mohammed Ali and Mike Tyson.

- Bodybuilders Lee Haney, Mike Christian and Tom Platz.
- Baseball players Rod Carew, Nolan Ryan, George Brett, Maury Wills, Don Sutton and Mark McGwire.
- Basketball coach Phil Jackson and tennis star Jimmy Connors and golfers Jack Nicklaus and Tiger Woods.

Celebrities who beat their smoking habit through hypnosis: Chelsea Handler, Mark Knopfler, Matt Damon, Drew Barrymore, Ellen DeGeneres, Ben Affleck, Ashton Kutcher, Ewan McGregor, Adele and Charlize Theron and former President Barack Obama.

Celebrities who have used hypnotherapy for personal improvement:
- Martha Stewart underwent hypnosis for recurring nightmares and was able to overcome them.
- Sylvester Stallone worked with the famous hypnotherapist Gil Boyne while filming Rocky in 1975.
- Hollywood actor Aaron Eckhart has credited hypnosis with changing his life forever after he used the practice to give up smoking and alcohol.
- Kevin Costner flew his personal hypnotist to Hawaii to cure his seasickness.
- Jackie Kennedy Onassis used hypnotherapy to relive and let go of tragic events in her life.
- Reese Witherspoon has used hypnosis to overcome her insecurities. According to the Cambridge Times website, the 38-year-old actress said that years of being told she was too fat or short for Hollywood roles took their toll

on her self-esteem, so she turned to hypnotherapy for
a confidence boost before taking on the role of Cheryl
Strayed in Wild.

- Jessica Alba, pregnant with her second child used hypnobirthing. Hypnobirthing was created by Marie Mongan,
a Certified Hypnotherapist and is used throughout the
world.

- Gisele Bundchen used hypnobirthing too. Tom Brady's
Parents are registered hypnobirthing educators and
practitioners.

I have had many amazing experiences using hypnotherapy to
help people, but nothing even comes close to using hypnobirthing to help my own daughter Brittney with the delivery of her
two children. She came to me terrified because every woman
she had ever met who had been through childbirth told her
terrible stories about pain and misery. She said she wanted a
natural childbirth, but was afraid of the pain.

I was taking pre-and post-surgery hypnotherapy certification at
the time and the amazing teacher, Lisa Machenberg, CHt also
taught hypnobirthing so I bought her outline and took Britt
through six sessions. This was a critical time. Her husband, Joe,
was deployed in Iraq with his Marine unit and her mom was her
coach. The experience was amazing. There was not zero pain,
but it was over in about 24 minutes. The nurses handled the
entire delivery because the doctor didn't get there in time.

So, when the opportunity arose again with Brittney's second pregnancy, we jumped right in. This time we included hubby. The longest part of this delivery was the three hours of labor building up to a sufficient dilation. Once there, the three pushes were over 15 minutes, the baby shot out and the doctor caught her! During this time, Britt had the recording of the hypnotherapy session playing out loud. The nurses and doctor were amazed, even more so when Britt told them it was her dad.

So there you have it, a detailed list of things, issues, problems and solutions that hypnotherapy can be used for. This is by no means an exhaustive list. Hopefully these details help you understand just how powerful and ubiquitous this modality is, and how you might be able to put it to work in your life.

CHAPTER SIX

Why Hypnotherapy Is Good for You

The information covered thus far is part of the human condition. No doubt you have experienced some or all of the conditions, circumstances, and or events articulated in the preceding pages. Maybe you have struggled. Maybe you've tried everything. Maybe nothing has worked and you are resigned to live with your circumstances, stoically accepting that this is just the hand life dealt you. I want you to know there is hope.

Many of my clients come to me having tried everything. One client was in psychotherapy for nine years! I asked her if around year three she might have wondered if it was going to work. Another client suffered for eight years taking the opioids her doctor had prescribed as the only method to control the pain associated with her list of symptoms.

The goal of this book is to spread the word about just how applicable and approachable hypnotherapy is for a wide range of issues and that there is, indeed, something definitive you can do to take back your life and take charge of your health and or your behavioral issues.

Maybe you haven't tried anything yet. This is the typical tough-guy approach. Hope it goes away and tell no one. But this behavior isn't limited to just guys. Many people suffer in silence because they are hopeful or think they can ride it out. Maybe they are embarrassed. The problem is that very few issues, especially issues related to the subconscious, will just go away. In fact, the longer they go unattended, the worse they tend to get. Even if the issues don't necessarily get worse, they will get entrenched. The behavior or issue becomes ingrained, like the contours of a well-worn path. As we discussed, the subconscious mind likes the known and fears the unknown, and physically, the body wants to come back to homeostasis. Doing nothing is not a viable option. It will lead to more problems, or a worsening of existing conditions. And further, dejected resignation can be completely disempowering.

In this age where the first response of so many people is reaching for a pill, many of them are now turning away from chemical therapies. The human body and its internal chemistry has an intelligence not found in chemicals synthesized in a lab. Maybe you are ready to join the tens of thousands who are pursuing natural approaches to health and wellness in the form of acupuncture, Ayurveda, naturopathic medicine, or one of the many other holistic modalities and you want something natural. Hypnotherapy is in alignment with natural modalities for health and wellness. Hypnotherapy is organic, non-invasive and non-chemical (except to the extent that it helps you reconfigure your own neurochemistry to get back into alignment).

Complementary and Alternative Medicine (CAM) is a group of diverse medical and health care systems, practices, and products that are not generally considered part of conventional medicine yet for which there is verifiable evidence of safety and treatment effectiveness. As we have seen, there are literally thousands of studies on the use and application of hypnotherapy. For the evidence-based community, there are brain scans and clinical descriptions. There are studies and findings, and no reason to question the power or effectiveness of hypnotherapy.

In December 2002, the National Center for Complementary and Integrative Health (NCCIH) and the National Center for Health Statistics (part of the Centers for Disease Control and Prevention) began collecting data on Americans' use of complementary and alternative medicine (CAM). The findings are from the 2012 National Health Interview Survey (NHIS), an annual in-person survey of Americans regarding their health and illness related experiences. The study showed that among U.S. adults aged 18 and over in 2002, 2007, and 2012, the percentage who used any complementary health approach in the past 12 months ranged from 32.3% in 2002 to 35.5% in 2007 and was most recently 33.2% in 2012.

Although terms are fuzzy and responses are sometimes difficult to categorize accurately, these approaches range from supplements to yoga to deep breathing techniques. Some are self-administered and others facilitated by a practitioner. Nevertheless, as of 2012, a third of Americans were using some form of alternative medicine for their health and wellness. I would venture to say that number has increased significantly in the last eight years despite the small dip between 2007 and 2012. So, the use of natural treatments is substantial and growing, and hypnotherapy is no exception. The problem is often that people tend to malign what they do not understand, or they need to overcomplicate things and dismiss anything that acts on simple principles.

One of the reasons so many of my clients come to me after having tried everything else is because they have chased treatment for symptoms. This is no knock against them, they know what they are experiencing and articulate it, but they often lack context, even though the details are from their own life. There is rarely a linear connection between the symptoms and the underlying issue, and my greatest skill is in interviewing thoroughly and connecting seemingly unrelated dots. And almost universally they tell me that previous providers never took the time to ask the deeper questions, never explored family dynamics and early childhood experiences.

In the modern healthcare setting very little time is allocated for visits, and rarely do the kind of details that give clues to long term subconscious programming come to light. What people experience is a series of symptomatic treatments that work for a while, but always seem to give rise to something else. It's like a giant game of whack-a-mole, only with your health or well-being.

If health plans would cover hypnotherapy it could lead to drastic cuts in healthcare costs when long-term healing takes place and chronic issues are resolved. The recognition is progress, but when it is supported by coverage real progress will have been made.

But you want something lasting, you are ready to get your life back so that you can live to your fullest potential, unburdened by the bad programming on your human hard drive placed there by someone you no longer know or care about, and causing behavior or illness that you no longer want. Getting to the root cause of issues through hypnotherapy will help you resolve long unresolved issues that have been holding you back from becoming the greatest version of yourself.

Are you ready for change? So many of my clients, as I have said time and again, come to me as a last resort, having tried so many other things. They are ready for change and when they achieve it, the results are sometimes very emotional.

A client who no longer experienced the debilitating symptoms of unexplained autoimmune disorder came back for another session. I asked if she was still experiencing pain. She said no. I asked her what she wanted to work on. She said motivation, she had been homebound, depressed, sleeping in and on pain meds for so many years she needed some help with motivation to get up and go out and attack the world! One of my proudest moments as a hypnotherapist was watching this woman blossom again. She is traveling, going out with friends, active with her adult children, and all over social media showing the world what she has going on.

Hypnotherapy is a powerful tool to help you achieve lasting change. When you address the long held issues, when you overwrite the old programming, when you finally get to the root cause of what has been ailing/troubling/holding you back, you will feel like you got your life back. I have seen it. Are you ready to get your life back?

Finally, do you want to be in control? The fallacy of construction that you can take a pill and it will magically make you better is a trap. You are not in control of the pills, they are in control of you. Very few prescriptions cure anything, mostly they just mask symptoms and end up placing you in a hamster wheel stuck forever in a routine of medicating. Don't get me wrong, the wonders of modern medicine are, well, wonderful. They just aren't always the best approach and seldom do they empower you to be in control. Nor are they the only treatment that can help. Even used in conjunction with necessary medicine hypnotherapy can be very effective.

Hypnotherapy is empowering. Hypnotherapy puts you in control. Since all hypnosis is self-hypnosis (the hypnotherapist is just there to help you facilitate the trance) it is ultimately you who are in control, often for the first time in a long time.

CHAPTER SEVEN

What the Hell Are You Waiting For?

So, now you know hypnotherapy's place in history, the long history from primitive mankind to the modern era. You know that through it all, the trance state, a basic human condition, remains largely the same as when it was first leveraged for healing by early healers and practitioners of medicine.

You know that hypnosis has been scrutinized, studied, criticized, ridiculed, mocked and made fun of. You know it has been utilized to heal, to treat, to entertain and yes, sometimes to manipulate. But it remains one of the most powerful organic, non-invasive and non-chemical modalities known to humans.

Hypnotherapy will continue to be an effective approach to human problems and issues for as long as there are humans. In all likelihood, the programmers who are conjuring up the details of artificial intelligence that will soon overrun our world are writing programs that will put people in trance, if they haven't already done so. Better to get ahead of the curve so you know what to expect and even have strategies to deal with this when it inevitably comes your way!

You also know what hypnotherapy is: a focused concentration while deeply relaxed, a dreamlike trance state wherein you drift between your inner world and your outer awareness. A state where you do not experience a loss of control; instead, you participate in an imagery conversation with your subconscious mind and engage all your senses to help override old programming that has held you back or made you sick.

You know that hypnotherapy is a gateway to unlock the answers to questions that may have plagued you since your childhood. You know that trance can be a safe place to release repressed emotions that have led to illness or unwanted behavior.

As for the science behind hypnotherapy, you can judge for yourself if the case has been made that there is sufficient scientific evidence to employ it in your own health and wellness regime. I tried to give context for how hypnosis fits in with the trajectory of science, and how modern science has attempted to describe, test, and utilize hypnotherapy to the benefit of those who need it.

Some will never be convinced or satisfied. Their overactive, over analytical minds will just not accept that there is merit to this ancient technique. These people are the slim margin of the population who cannot be hypnotized. I believe everyone can be hypnotized if they want to be. Some just do not.

So many people demand an overly complex explanation, a highly technical solution to their problems. If it were that easy, they would have just willed whatever was hurting them better a long time ago. I have heard this many times in response to the question, "Are you ready to let it go?" Writing a new story is within the grasp of everyone if they want to change their current story. The problem is we become heavily invested in our story. With the expansion of social media, some people post every detail of their ailments and their problems. Some people come to identify with their conditions. Remember, the subconscious loves the known and the unknown is scary. Carolyn Myss has written extensively about our propensity to identify with our problems and over share them with anyone who will listen. She has several resources on YouTube on Why We Don't Heal, and her book *Anatomy of the Spirit* is fantastic on the subject.

This is an amazing time for hypnotherapy because there is finally enough technology, and science has advanced enough to be able to fully explain what is going on during trance. This will only grow and expand. The only thing lagging is the wide dissemination of information about hypnotherapy on a scale sufficient to inspire more people to adopt it into their lives.

We have also covered the range of human conditions that hypnotherapy can help. Without overselling here, hypnotherapy can be applicable to all human endeavors. I usually explain that it can take you where you want to go; it can get you out of where you no longer want to be; it can help you relax even better than sleep, and it can reduce your stress and anxiety better than any pill or drug.

We covered the general areas of application as well as some of the emerging uses of hypnotherapy. The most heavily utilized also happen to be the most widely studied. As a result, there is quite a bit of research on certain areas of hypnotherapy, like irritable bowel syndrome and other gut related issues, cancer pain, trauma, behavioral change like weight loss and smoking cessation. But there is growing interest in hypnotherapy's application to autoimmune disease, and a whole range of stress related conditions, among others.

At this point you should have a good idea why you should use hypnotherapy. Remember - life is a contact sport and not only do none of us get out alive, we pick up a lot of scars and baggage along the way. It is hard not to have our well-being influenced by the events that make up our experience.

Going back to Dr Joe's show Rewired, he presented an excellent summary of why we get stuck and find it so difficult to make change. Memory is very unreliable. What we remember are not the factual details of an event that affected us; what we remember is how it made us feel. The chemical response of our body produced a set of feelings and emotions and that is why we remember how an event made us feel. We will mold the details in our mind to fit how we felt. This changes over time and is affected by other emotions like sentimentality. So, if I asked you why you did something the way you did it and you say that this happened to you 20 years ago and you always react this way when that happens, you are being controlled by an unreal memory.

The problem is that you don't remember it the way it happened. You remember it the way it made you feel. So, you are living in a past that didn't happen the way you think it did and now, your future behavior becomes predictable based upon what you think is your past. You are essentially living a predictable future based upon a false past that, taken together, rob you of the present moment. Most of us do not even know this cycle is going on. Worse, even if we did fully understand it, no part of society or schooling teaches us how to change it even if we knew what was really going on.

To fully understand the events of your past, you need to put them into the context of your life and take constructive steps to make lasting change by creating new thoughts that create new choices, that create new behavior, that in turn create new thoughts. This is being present and living intentionally. Meditation is a great avenue to begin this process, but it is hypnotherapy that will help you anchor the change so that it is lasting and you can move forward into your best self. It is a complementary component of a mind/body/spirit practice. Because the experience of trance is a combination of inner world and outer awareness, it is almost its own metaphor, to the extent that hypnotherapy is a tool to connect our inner world and our outer awareness. When we can become congruent in our inner and outer worlds, consistent with our minds and our bodies, health is what follows. Dis-ease is held at bay as our powerful immune systems do their job and protect us from an increasingly toxic environment.

As we learn about the body's innate intelligence and how our neurochemistry and neurocircuitry carry on expansive and instantaneous communications within, hypnotherapy can be seen as a language to communicate with our body's inner intelligence. Energy healing, chakra alignment, meditation and mindfulness are all amazing modalities for health and wellness, and hypnotherapy goes hand-in-hand in this mind/body spirit continuum.

My own personal healing crisis led me to study and apply hypnotherapy in the service of others and I am amazed at how effective it is in improving the lives of others. I feel blessed to have found a path to be in service. I used to be one of those people who over thought and over analyzed everything and didn't think anything that wasn't connected to the latest and greatest technology could be beneficial but practicing this ancient technique has taught me otherwise. I am truly grateful.

I use hypnotherapy to help others daily, and in countless ways. I have conducted hypnotherapy sessions with people from all over the world via the video conference platform Zoom. From New Zealand and Australia to England, Scotland and Canada, I am fortunate to have touched the lives of many. I have helped people as young as 10 and as old as 82, as well as victims of stroke, different diseases, and people preparing for surgery or recovering from it. I have also helped people with cancer, along with people who wanted to quit smoking so they didn't get cancer, and a range of human experience in between. All have been opportunities to love and help fellow human beings. There is nothing like it in the world when the light goes on and I reach an ah-ha moment when I have successfully helped someone connect dots from their life experience. Often, they never saw that causal relationship until that moment.

It is heartwarming to witness the tears while in hypnosis as a client connects with their inner child. I am just quiet for a while as they relive some forgotten memory. I once had a client who, after a deepener exercise, burst into laughter. I didn't know what to do. She was in cataleptic hypnosis and yet began to apologize through her laughter. She said she had been told that she laughed in her sleep, but she never really knew. I told her to go ahead, she probably needed it. Then I deployed a tactic I learned from my excellent training at HMI (after saying to myself, "What would Dr. Kappas do?). I told her that the more she laughed, the deeper into hypnosis she would go, and that with each laugh she would be twice as deep as just the moment before. She settled and we moved on with our work, but it is moments like these that makes me really love what I do.

Some hypnotherapists have invented other names for hypnosis. Maybe they are embarrassed, or they got tired of people making chicken quacking jokes, or they saw the opportunity for a slick marketing tactic. They call it rapid transformation or quantum healing or some other newfangled way to describe this ancient technique. As for me, I'll just keep replying that no, you won't see me at the state fair on stage making people cluck, and I proudly carry on with Norman Plotkin Hypnotherapy.

I hope to see you one day and look forward to helping you become the best version of you! Thank you for sticking it out and reading all the way through the book. It says something about you and your willingness to learn and apply proven methods for health and wellbeing. My hope in writing this book has been to share this wonderful modality with others so that they might see it in a different light, and so that they might be inclined to put it to work in their life for positive benefit. Or maybe pass along what they learned to someone they care about so that person might put it to work in their lives.

However you use this information, I wish you long life and happiness and many hypnotic moments toward health and prosperity!

Acknowledgments

Many of us dream of someday writing a book, but fulfilling the dream is very difficult as a practical matter, as everyone who has yet to complete theirs can attest. To get across the finish line, we need those who stand with us.

My dream became a reality because Britt believed, Tian pushed, and Diane supported (from the other side of the veil). It is one thing to understand the principle of Occam's Razor, that the simplest explanation is the best explanation and another thing altogether to put it into practice. Thank you all for helping my dream come true for a second time. I'm on a roll!

I did not hear life's whisper, and so it yelled, and in that yell was the seed of my transformation, which turned out to be an unwrapped gift. That gift changed my life and continues to make its presence known on an ongoing basis.

To the authors of the many books I read to come to an understanding of the power of the subconscious mind, our own involvement in healing and the mind-body connection, a heartfelt thank you for your groundbreaking work; your belief in the human mind, body, and spirit; and your willingness to share even when it wasn't always popular to do so.

And to all those who seek answers and wellness, my hope is that you find usefulness and inspiration from these pages. I hold encouragement and love for you.

About the Author

Norman Plotkin is a former lobbyist and cancer survivor who has found his passion for helping people through practicing hypnotherapy, coaching, speaking, and writing around wellness, healing, and recovery.

During a 25-year career in and around state government, Norman gained powerful insights into health policy and the internal workings of the practice of medicine as a committee consultant to the California State Assembly Health Committee and a lobbyist for the California Medical Association.

Norman is certified in hypnotherapy as well as for a number of sub specialties including for cancer clients. His offering includes coaching on the proven factors that make a real difference for anyone with chronic illness for true healing and recovery. On his journey, he discovered that the power of the therapeutic partnership is established when people become active participants in the development of their therapeutic plan, because they feel more in control of their own well-being and are more likely to make sustained lifestyle changes to improve their health.

Norman's ultimate goal is that his experience and research will enable him to positively impact the lives of those who present having tried everything to get relief as well as their families.

Norman has an amazing partner, Tian, who is an Acupuncturist and Herbalist and practitioner of Traditional Chinese Medicine, three children and two grandchildren. One of his most amazing life experiences was taking his daughter through hypnobirthing, twice! Thus delivering on his daughter's desire for natural childbirth without drugs. He lives in Sacramento, CA, where he can be found, when not writing, speaking or seeing clients, cutting through traffic on his Yamaha.

Connect with Norman at: www.normanplotkin.

Thank You

Thanks so much for reading. The fact that you've gotten to this point in the book tells me something important about you: you're ready. You're ready to shift out of overwhelm and quit feeling like a helpless victim. You're ready to experience participation in and ownership of your health and wellness.

Please visit my website to learn helpful information to keep you on track as you engage in your own health and wellness: www.normanplotkin.com.

Made in the USA
Monee, IL
30 March 2021